# Descriptive Physical Oceanography

# Descriptive Physical Oceanography

AN INTRODUCTION

by

GEORGE L. PICKARD

M.A., D.Phil.

*Professor of Physics*

*Director of the Institute of Oceanography*
*University of British Columbia*

THE QUEEN'S AWARD
TO INDUSTRY 1966

# PERGAMON PRESS

OXFORD · LONDON · EDINBURGH · NEW YORK

TORONTO · SYDNEY · PARIS · BRAUNSCHWEIG

Pergamon Press Ltd., Headington Hill Hall, Oxford
4 & 5 Fitzroy Square, London W.1
Pergamon Press (Scotland) Ltd., 2 & 3 Teviot Place, Edinburgh 1
Pergamon Press Inc., 44-01 21st Street, Long Island City, New York 11101
Pergamon of Canada Ltd., 207 Queen's Quay West, Toronto 1
Pergamon Press (Aust.) Pty. Ltd., Rushcutters Bay,
Sydney, New South Wales
Pergamon Press S.A.R.L., 24 rue des Écoles, Paris 5e
Vieweg & Sohn GmbH, Burgplatz 1, Braunschweig

Copyright © 1963 Pergamon Press Ltd.
First edition 1963
Reprinted 1966
Reprinted 1968
Library of Congress Catalog Card No. 63-22645

*Printed in Great Britain by Thomas Nelson (Printers) Ltd., Edinburgh*

08 101759 6 (flexicover)
08 201759 X (hard cover)

# Contents

# Preface

THE DEVELOPMENT of interest in oceanography in recent years has led to an increased demand from students for information on the subject. The texts available hitherto have been either more elementary in treatment or more comprehensive and extensive than may be desirable for an introduction to the subject for the undergraduate. The present text is an attempt to supply information on the Synoptic or Descriptive aspects of Physical Oceanography at a level suitable for undergraduates in the sciences and possibly for senior school students who wish to learn something of the aims and achievements of this field of scientific study.

In presenting the synoptic approach it must be emphasized that this represents only one aspect of physical oceanography. The other, and complementary one, is the dynamical approach through the laws of mechanics. This is described by Dr. R. W. Burling in *Dynamical Oceanography*, the companion volume to the present one in this series. The student who requires a full introduction to physical oceanography should read both volumes.

The text is intended to be introductory to the subject. For the student in physics and mathematics it should serve to present to him the main aspects of the field before he proceeds to the more advanced texts and original literature making free use of mathematical methods. For the student in the biological sciences it may supply sufficient information on descriptive physical oceanography to provide the necessary background for his studies of the fauna and flora of the sea.

If the reader concludes the text with a feeling that our knowledge of the sea is incomplete at present, one of the author's objectives will have been achieved. This was to indicate to the student that there is still much to be learned of the ocean and that if he is interested in observing the marine world and interpreting it there are still many opportunities for him to do so.

For the student who wishes to extend his study of physical oceanography suggestions for further reading are given at the end of this book. These suggestions are chiefly to textbooks which enlarge on many aspects described in the present one and contain references to the original literature for those who have access to it.

The text is based on a course presented by the author for eight years at the University of British Columbia to introduce undergraduate and graduate students to synoptic oceanography. It owes much to the more comprehensive text *The Oceans*, by Sverdrup, Johnson and Fleming, and the author wishes to acknowledge this and also the stimulation received during a year at the Scripps Institution of Oceanography. The author is particularly indebted to Dr. J. P. Tully of the Pacific Oceanographic Group for initiating him into oceanography and for encouragement since, and to Dr. R. W. Burling for reading the manuscript and offering many constructive comments.

G.L.P.

CHAPTER ONE

# Introduction

OCEANOGRAPHY is the general name given to the scientific study of the oceans, with an emphasis on their character as an environment. It is conveniently divided in terms of the basic sciences into physical oceanography, biological oceanography, chemical oceanography and geological oceanography. This book is concerned primarily with one aspect of the first of these.

The basic goal of oceanographic study is to obtain a clear and systematic description of the oceans, sufficiently quantitative to permit us to predict their behaviour in the future with some certainty. While we can do this in a general fashion for some characteristics and in some regions, we are a long way from being able to predict details with confidence. In other words, there is still a great deal of scientific study of the oceans to be done and understanding to be achieved.

Generally the individual scientist studying the ocean devotes himself to investigations in one of the sciences, but very often supporting information may be obtained from observations in other sciences. In fact, one of the intriguing aspects of oceanography is that it is not yet too highly compartmented or specialized, and there is much co-operation between those working in the different sciences.

There are many reasons for developing our knowledge of the oceans. As sources of food, of chemicals and of power, they are as yet only exploited to a very minor degree. They are still a vitally important avenue of transportation and are always likely to be. They form a sink into which industrial waste is dumped, but they do not form a bottomless pit into which material like radioactive waste can be thrown without due thought being given to where it may be carried by currents. The vast heat capacity of the oceans exerts a significant effect on the climate of the land, while the continuous movement of the currents and waves along the coast must be taken into account when piers, breakwaters and other structures are built.

In all these applications, and in many others, a knowledge of the circulation of the oceans is needed. The goal of the physical oceanographer is to obtain a systematic quantitative description of the character of the ocean waters and of their movements. The latter include the major ocean currents which circulate continuously but with fluctuating velocity, they include the variable coastal currents, the reversing tidal currents, the rise and fall of the tide and the waves generated by wind or earthquake. The character of the ocean waters includes those aspects, such as temperature and salt content, which determine density and hence vertical movement, and also includes dissolved substances or biological species in so far as they yield information about the currents.

The physical study of the ocean is approached in two ways. In what is called the synoptic or descriptive approach observations are made of specific features and these are reduced to as simple a statement as possible of the features themselves and of their relations to other features. The dynamical or theoretical approach is to apply the already known laws of physics to the ocean, regarding it as a body acted upon by forces, and to endeavour to solve the resulting mathematical equations to obtain information on the motions to be expected from the forces acting. In practice there are limitations and difficulties associated with both methods, and our present knowledge of the oceans has been developed by a combination of the synoptic and the dynamical approaches. The method is as follows. Preliminary observations give one some idea what features of the ocean require explanation. The basic physical law which is considered to apply to the situation is then used to set up an equation between the forces acting and the motions observed. A solution of this equation, even an approximate one, will give some idea of how the motions may vary in time or space. It may also suggest further observations which may be made to test whether the law selected or the features entered into the equation are adequate or not. If not, the theory is modified in the light of the test observations and the procedure of alternate observation of nature and development of the theory is pursued until a satisfactory theory is obtained. The method is typical of scientific research.

Our present knowledge in physical oceanography represents an accumulation of data, most of which have been gathered during the past hundred years. The purpose of this book is to summarize some of these data to give an idea of what we now know about the distribution of the physical characteristics of the ocean waters and of their circulation. The achievements of the alternate but parallel approach through the laws of mechanics are described by Burling in *Dynamical Oceanography*, the companion volume in this series.

During its history physical oceanography has gone through several phases. Presumably ever since man started to sail the oceans he has been concerned with ocean currents as they affect the course of his ship. This distinctly practical approach is more a branch of the related field of hydrography, which includes the preparation of navigation charts and of current and tide tables, than of oceanography, but out of it came the study of the currents for the purpose of determining *why* they behave in the way they do as well as *how*. Many of the earlier navigators, such as Cook and Vancouver, made valuable scientific observations during their voyages in the late 1700's, but it is generally considered that Mathew Fontaine Maury in about 1860 started the systematic large scale collection of ocean current data, using ship's navigation logs as his source of information. Many physical data on surface currents and winds were collected, and still are, from this source. The first major expedition designed expressly to study all the scientific aspects of the oceans was that of H.M.S. *Challenger* which circumnavigated the globe from 1872 to 1876. The first large scale expedition organized primarily to gather physical oceanographic data was the German *Meteor* expedition to study the Atlantic Ocean from 1925 to 1927.

Some of the earliest theoretical studies of the sea were of the surface tides by Newton (1687) and Laplace (1775), and of waves by Gerstner (1802) and Stokes (1874). Following this, about 1896, some of the Scandinavian meteorologists started to turn their attention to the ocean, since dynamical meteorology and dynamical oceanography have much in common. The present basis for dynamical oceanography owes much to the early work of Bjerknes, Helland-Hansen, Ekman and others.

In recent years attention has been given to other phases, including the circulation and water properties at the ocean boundaries along the coasts and in estuaries, and also in the deep and bottom waters of the oceans. The coastal waters are more accessible for observation than the open ocean but show much larger fluctuations in space and time, and also present more difficulties for theoretical study. The deep and bottom waters are very difficult to observe: this makes it hard to acquire information to start the theoretical studies, and also to test them.

The plan followed in this book will be to describe briefly the ocean basins and something of their topography as it affects ocean circulation, and then to introduce some of the terminology of physical oceanography. After a brief summary of the properties of sea water, a general description of the distribution of water characteristics, both in the vertical and in the horizontal, will be presented to give the reader some feeling for typical conditions. A discussion of the sources of gain or loss of heat and of water to the ocean follows, and then a description of instruments and of methods of data presentation. After this there is a description of the water characteristics and of the currents in the individual oceans of the world, and finally a few comments on the present state of our knowledge in descriptive physical oceanography.

Perhaps a comment upon the title of this book should be made before proceeding. Among oceanographers the term "synoptic oceanography" is understood to refer to the method of approach which starts with the observation of data and then continues with the preparation of a concise description, i.e. a "synopsis". But description and synopsis are only the start. The oceanographer then seeks regularities in the data and interprets the distributions of properties with the object of obtaining information on the circulation. Therefore a more exact title for this aspect would be "Interpretative Oceanography", but unfortunately this term is not in general use. "Synoptic Oceanography" was the first choice for a title and would be clear in its meaning to oceanographers. However, this book is not intended for trained oceanographers but for would-be oceanographers or for those who wish to introduce themselves to this aspect of science. In the end, the title "Descriptive Physical Oceanography" was chosen in the hope that this would best indicate the character of its contents to those who were not yet familiar with the field. It is hoped, however, that the reader who completes its study will no longer be a novice but will by then appreciate that "synoptic" oceanography does not stop at description but continues with its main aim, interpretation.

# CHAPTER TWO

# Ocean Dimensions, Shapes and Bottom Materials

THE OCEANS are basins in the surface of the solid earth containing salt water. The purpose of this chapter is to introduce some of the nomenclature and to direct attention to some features of the basins which have a close connection with the circulation and are of importance to the physical oceanographer. A more detailed description of the geology and geophysics of the ocean basins is given in another book in this series, *Submarine Geology* by Keen.

In order to appreciate the shapes of the oceans and seas it is almost essential to examine them on a globe, since map projections on to flat paper always introduce distortions when large portions of the earth are to be represented. From the oceanographic point of view it is convenient to distinguish the various regions in terms of their oceanographic characteristics, particularly their circulations.

Anticipating the information which will be given in later chapters, the major ocean areas will be defined now as the Southern Ocean, the Atlantic Ocean, the Pacific Ocean, the Indian Ocean, and the Arctic Sea. The last four are clearly divided from each other by land masses but the divisions between the Southern Ocean and the others to its north are determined only by the characteristics of the ocean waters and by their circulation as will be described in Chapter 7. Then there are smaller bodies of water such as the Mediterranean Sea, the Gulf of Mexico, the Bering Sea, etc., which are clearly bounded by land or by island chains. The term "sea" is also used for a

portion of an ocean which is not divided off but has local distinguish-
ing oceanographic characteristics.    Examples are the Norwegian,
the Labrador and the Tasman Seas.

Looking at a globe again, it is evident that more of the earth's
surface is covered by sea than by land, about 71% compared to
29%.  Furthermore, the proportion of water to land in the southern
hemisphere is much greater (4:1) than in the northern hemisphere
(1·5:1).  In area, the Pacific Ocean is about as large as the Atlantic
and the Indian Oceans combined.  If one includes the neighbouring
sectors of the Southern Ocean with the three main oceans north of
it, then the Pacific Ocean occupies about 46% of the total world
ocean area, the Atlantic Ocean about 23%, the Indian Ocean about
20%, and the rest combined about 11%.

The average depth of the oceans is close to 4000 metres while
the seas are generally about 1200 metres deep or less.  Relative to
sea level the oceans are much deeper than the land is high.  While
only 11% of the land surface of the earth is more than 2000 metres
above sea level, 84% of the sea bottom is more than 2000 metres
deep.    However, the maxima are more similar: the height of
Mt. Everest is about 8840 metres while the maximum depth recorded in the oceans is 11,524 metres by H.M.S. *Cook* in the
Mindanao Trench in the western Pacific.

Although the average depth of the oceans, 4 km, is a considerable
distance, it is small compared to the horizontal dimensions of the
oceans, which are of the order of 5000 to 15,000 km.    An idea of
the relative dimensions of the Pacific Ocean may be obtained by
stating that they are much the same as a sheet of lightweight typing
paper.    This analogy makes the oceans appear as a very thin skin
on the surface of the earth.  Relative to the major dimensions of the
earth they are thin, but there is a great deal of detail and structure
in this thin layer between the surface and the bottom of the oceans.

Very often we wish to present some of these details by drawing
a vertical cross-section of a part of the oceans.  A drawing to true
scale would have the relative dimensions of the edge of a sheet of
paper and would either be too thin to show details or too long to

be convenient. Therefore we usually have to distort our cross-section by making the vertical scale much larger than the horizontal one. For instance we might use a scale of 1 cm on the paper to represent 100 km horizontally in the sea while depths might be at a scale of 1 cm to represent 100 m, i.e. 0·1 km. In this case the vertical dimensions on our drawing would be magnified by 1000 times compared to the horizontal ones. This gives us room to show the detail we wish but exaggerates the slope of the sea bottom or of lines of constant property drawn on the cross-section. It is

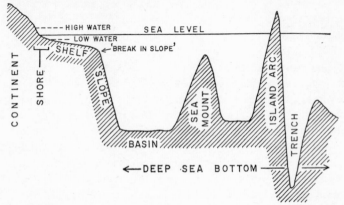

FIG. 1. *Section through ocean floor to show principal features schematically.*

as well to remind oneself occasionally that such slopes are in reality far less than they appear on the cross-section drawings. For instance, a line of constant temperature with a real slope of 1 in 100 would be exceptionally steep in the ocean, one of 1 in 1000 very steep, and 1 in 10,000 more usual.

The continents form the major lateral boundaries to the oceans, and the detailed features of the shoreline and of the sea bottom are important in their effects on circulation. Starting from the land, the main divisions recognized are the shore, the continental shelf, the continental slope and the deep-sea bottom (shown schematically in Fig. 1).

The *shore* is defined here as that part of the land mass close to the sea which has been modified by the action of the sea. It is as well to note in this connection that there is ample evidence to indicate that sea level in the past has varied over a range of about 100 m when glaciers were smaller or larger than they are now. The beach is the seaward limit of the shore and extends roughly from the highest to the lowest tide levels. Sandy beaches are often in a state of dynamic equilibrium. That is to say, they may be composed of sand all the time but it may not always be the same sand. This may be continually moving along the shore under the influence of waves and nearshore currents. This state is very often made evident by the way in which sand accumulates against new structures built on the shore, or by the way in which it is removed from a beach when a breakwater is built in such a way as to cut off the supply of sand beyond it. On some beaches, the sand may be removed by currents associated with high waves at one season of the year and replaced by different currents associated with lower waves at another season.

The *continental shelf* extends seaward from the shore with an average gradient of 1 in 500. Its outer limit (the "break-in-slope") is set where the gradient increases to about 1 in 20 on the average to form the continental slope down to the deep-sea bottom. The shelf has an average width of 65 km. In places it is much narrower than this, while in others, as in the Bering Sea or the Arctic shelf off northern Siberia it is much wider. The bottom material is dominantly sand, with rock or mud being less common. The division between the shelf and the slope is made on the basis of the break-in-slope which is usually clearly evident when one examines a vertical cross-section of the sea bottom from the shore outward. The average depth at the break-in-slope is about 130 m. Most of the world's fisheries are located on the continental shelf.

The *continental slope* averages about 4000 m vertically from the shelf to the deep-sea bottom, but in places extends as much as 9000 m vertically in a relatively short horizontal distance. In general the continental slope is considerably steeper than the slopes from lowlands to highlands on land. The material of the slope is predominantly mud, with some rock outcrops. Very typical features of the shelf and slope are the submarine canyons which are of world-wide occurrence. They are valleys in the slope, either V-shaped or with vertical sides, and are usually found off coasts with rivers and never off desert areas.

The *deep-sea bottom* is the last and most extensive area. Depths of 3000 to 6000 m are found over 76% of the ocean basins, with 1% being deeper. Perhaps the most characteristic aspect of the deep-sea bottom is the variety of its topography. Before any significant deep ocean soundings were available the sea bottom was regarded as uniformly smooth. When detailed sounding started in connection with cable laying, it became clear that this was not the case and there was a swing to regarding the sea bottom as predominantly rugged. Neither view is exclusively correct, for we know now that there are mountains, valleys and plains on the ocean bottom just as on land. The characteristic features are, as on land, either basically long and narrow (welts and furrows) or of roughly equal lateral extent (swells and basins). The Mid-ocean Ridge is probably the most extensive single feature of the earth's topography. Starting south of Greenland it extends along the middle of the Atlantic from north to south and then through the Indian and Pacific Oceans. In the Atlantic it separates the bottom waters, as can be seen from their very different properties east and west of the ridge (Fig. 24).

The opposite of the ridge is the trench. The majority of the deep ones are in the Pacific, including the Aleutian, Kurile, Philippine and Marianas Trenches, with a few in other oceans such as the Puerto Rico and the South Sandwich Trenches in the Atlantic, and the Sunda Trench in the Indian Ocean. The greatest depths in the oceans occur in these trenches. They are often shaped like an arc of a circle in plan form and are usually associated with an arc of islands on one side.

Individual mountains ("seamounts") are widely distributed in the oceans. Some project above the surface to form islands, while the tops of others are below the surface.

In some of the large basins the sea floor is very smooth, possibly more so than the plains areas on land. Stretches of the abyssal plain in the western North Atlantic have been measured to be smooth within 2 m, the present limit of sounding accuracy, over distances of 100 km.

Our present knowledge of the shape of the ocean floor results from an accumulation of sounding measurements, most of which have been made within the last 40 years. The early measurements were made by lowering a weight on a measured line until the weight touched bottom. This method was slow; in deep water it was uncertain because it was difficult to tell when the weight touched the bottom, and to be certain that the line was vertical. Since 1920 most depth measurements have been made with echo-sounders which measure the time taken for a pulse of sound to go from ship to bottom and be reflected back to the ship. One half of this time is multiplied by the speed of sound in sea water to give the depth. With present day equipment, the time can be measured very accurately and the main uncertainty over a flat bottom is in the value to be used for the speed of sound. This varies with water temperature and salinity and if these are not measured at the time of sounding an average value must be used. This introduces a possibility of error. Over trenches or places where rapid changes in depth occur there may also be some uncertainty about whether the echo comes from directly under the ship (to give the true depth) or from one side.

On the continental shelf and slope, most of the *bottom material* comes directly from the land, either brought down by rivers or blown by the wind. The material of the deep sea bottom is often more finely divided than that on the shelf or slope. Much of it is pelagic in character, i.e. it has been formed in the sea itself. The two major deep ocean sediments are the inorganic "red" clay and the organic oozes. The former has less than 30% of organic material and is mainly mineral in content. It consists of fine material from the land (which may have travelled great distances before finally settling out on to the bottom), volcanic material, and meteoric remains. The oozes are over 30% organic in origin from the remains of originally living organisms (plankton). The calcareous oozes have a high percentage of calcium carbonate from the shells of animal plankton, while the siliceous oozes have a high proportion of silica from the shells of planktonic plants and animals. The siliceous oozes are found mainly in the Southern Ocean and in the equatorial Pacific. In both of these regions, the distribution is clearly related to the water flow above—around Antarctica in the first case and parallel to the equator in the second.

Except when turbidity currents (mud slides from the slope) deposit their loads, the average rate of deposition of the sediments is from 0·1 to 10 mm per 1000 years, and much information on the past history of the oceans is stored up in them. Samples of bottom material are obtained with a "corer"—a steel pipe 2 to 30 m long which is lowered vertically and forced to penetrate into the sediments by the heavy weight at its upper end. The "core" of sediment retained in the pipe may represent material deposited over a period from 100,000 to 10 million years per metre of its length. Sometimes the material is layered, indicating stages of sedimentation of different materials. In some places layers of volcanic ash can be related to historical records of eruptions; in others, organisms characteristic of cold or of warm waters are found in different layers and suggest changes in temperature of the overlying water during the period represented by the core. In some places gradations from coarse to fine sediments in the upward direction suggest the occurrence of turbidity currents bringing material to the region with the coarser material settling out first and the finer later.

The physical oceanographer looks at the sediments for the information which they give him on the movement of the water above. This information may be of movements in the past. It may also give some idea of the mean flow, averaging out small fluctuations. The distribution of material around Antarctica is an example of this. The surface of the ocean bottom also reveals information. Photographs of the deep-sea bottom have been obtained in recent years and some of them show ripples such as one sees on a sand beach after the tide has gone out. Such ripples are only found on the beach where the water speed is quite considerable, such as in the backwash from waves. We conclude from the ripples on the deep-ocean bottom that currents of similar speed occur there. This discovery dispelled the earlier notion that all deep-sea currents are very slow.

CHAPTER THREE

# Physical Properties of Sea-water

## SALINITY AND CONDUCTIVITY

Sea-water is a complicated solution and contains the majority of the known elements. Some of the more abundant components are chloride ion $55\cdot0\%$ of the total dissolved material, sulphate ion $7\cdot7\%$, sodium ion $30\cdot6\%$, magnesium ion $3\cdot7\%$ and potassium ion $1\cdot1\%$. A significant feature of sea-water is that while the total concentration of dissolved salts varies from place to place, the ratios of the more abundant components remain almost constant. This may be taken as evidence that over geologic time the oceans have become well mixed, i.e. while there are well marked circulations within each ocean, water must also circulate between the oceans. At the same time there are significant differences in total concentration of the dissolved salts from place to place and at different depths. This indicates that processes must be continually in action to concentrate or dilute sea-water in specific localities; these processes are features of the sea which oceanographers wish to understand.

The total amount of dissolved material in sea-water is termed the "salinity" and is defined as "the total amount of solid materials in grams contained in one kilogram of sea-water when all the carbonate has been converted to oxide, the bromine and iodine replaced by chlorine and all organic matter completely oxidized." For example, the average salinity of ocean water is about $35\,\text{g}/\text{km}$

of sea-water, usually written as " $S = 35\%_0$ " and read as "thirty-five parts per thousand". The direct determination of salinity by evaporating sea-water to dryness is too difficult to carry out as a routine process. The method which was used from the beginning of the century until recently was to determine the amount of chloride ion ("chlorinity") by titration with silver nitrate and then to scale up to the salinity by the experimentally determined relation:

$$\text{Salinity} = 0\cdot03 + 1\cdot805 \times \text{Chlorinity}.$$

This is based on the measured ratio of chloride ion to total dissolved substances. Nowadays, most salinity determinations are made by determining the *electrical conductivity* of the sea-water and then using the known relation between conductivity and salinity to calculate the latter. The electrical conductivity is, however, very much dependent on the temperature of the sea-water and this has to be corrected for in the measurement. The real advances which permitted the change from chemical titration to the electrical salinometer were refinements of the electrical circuits to permit accurate compensation for temperature, and developments to reduce electrochemical effects at the the electrodes of the conductivity cell. A further improvement is the use of an electrodeless method of conductivity measurement described in Chapter 6, with compensation for temperature. This has now become the standard method for salinity determination. The accuracy of the titration method in routine use is about $\pm 0\cdot02\%_0$ in salinity (i.e. about $\pm 0\cdot06\%$ error in measurement), while by electrical conductivity it is about $\pm0\cdot003\%_0$ in salinity (i.e. $\pm0\cdot01\%$ error).

The present position with regard to our knowledge of the relations between the chlorinity, the density and the electrical conductivity of sea-water should be made clear. In 1884, Dittmar reported the results of his chemical analysis of seventy-seven samples of sea-water collected from around the world by the *Challenger* Expedition. These results supported the belief, expressed earlier by Forchhammer, that the ratios, one to another, of the concentrations of the major ions in sea-water are subject to only slight variations.

Some subsequent writers have rephrased this and implied that the ratios are exactly constant or have acted as though this were the case. That is to say they have assumed that there is an exact and constant relationship between the chlorinity, density and electrical conductivity of sea-water from any place in any ocean and from any depth. In a critical review of the situation in 1958, Carritt and Carpenter pointed out that this rephrasing is incorrect, and that Dittmar's results themselves indicate the possibility of small variations. Such variations may be of significance, particularly in the study of deep waters where the differences in properties are small. After Carritt and Carpenter's review, discussions of these matters made it clear that the time had come for the relations to be reinvestigated, both because of the advances in analytical techniques since Dittmar's time and because of the improvements made in the techniques for the measurement of the electrical conductivity of sea-water. In particular, it is now possible to get much more reproducible results for the electrical conductivity of sea-water on a routine basis than for the chlorinity even by precise titration.

The plan for the new study is to collect many hundreds of samples of sea-water from around the world and from different depths, and to measure for each the electrical conductivity and the density (at the National Institute of Oceanography in England) and the chlorinity (at the Department of Oceanography of Liverpool University). The study is not yet complete but about two hundred samples had been measured for conductivity and chlorinity by the end of 1961. The results, reported in February 1962, show that the ionic composition of sea-water is not constant but has small but significant variations from place to place and from surface to deep water. The adjective 'significant' here is used to indicate that enough measurements have been made of sufficient precision to be sure that the differences and fluctuations found in the results are real and not just a consequence of experimental errors. The reasons for the variations in ionic composition are not yet known. For the samples for which density has also been measured, it is found that the relationship between density and conductivity a little closer than between density and chlorinity. This is interpreted to mean that the chlorinity, i.e. the chemical composition, shows significant differences from place to place and with depth in the oceans. One of the factors used in arriving at this interpretation is that solutions of the major constituents of sea-water of the same concentration have very similar conductivities and densities. This means that the proportion of one ion to another may change, i.e. the chemical composition may change, but as long as the total weight of dissolved substances is the same the conductivity and the density will be unchanged.

Since one of the main reasons for determining either chlorinity or conductivity of sea-water is to deduce the density (which it is inconvenient to measure directly), the conclusion is that it would be better to do this from its electrical conductivity than from its chlorinity.

It should be emphasized that these results are preliminary and the conclusions tentative because the study is not yet complete, but they do seem to be significant and indicate that the composition of sea-water is not exactly constant.


## TEMPERATURE AND DENSITY

The second important physical characteristic of sea-water is its *temperature*. Some of the factors determining this characteristic are described in Chapter 5 and the techniques for measuring it in Chapter 6.

The physical oceanographer is particularly interested in the temperature and salinity of sea-water because they are characteristics which help to identify a particular water body, and also because together with pressure they determine the *density* of sea-water. The latter is important because it determines the depth at which a water mass will settle in equilibrium—the least dense at the top and the most dense at the bottom. Density is expressed physically in grams per cubic centimetre and in the open ocean values range from about 1·02400 to 1·03000 g/cm³. Lower values occur in coastal waters. As a matter of convenience it is usual in oceanography to quote only the last four of these figures in the form of a quantity called $\sigma_{s,t,p}$ defined as:

$$\sigma_{s,t,p} = (\text{density} - 1) \times 10^3$$

This is referred to as the *in situ* value. For many applications in synoptic oceanography the pressure effect on density can be ignored and a quantity $\sigma_{s,t,o}$ is used, commonly abbreviated to $\sigma_t$ (spoken as "sigma-tee" where the $t$ here represents temperature). This is the density difference of the water sample when the total pressure on it has been reduced to atmospheric (i.e. the water pressure $p = 0$) but the salinity and temperature are as *in situ*. The relationship between $\sigma_t$, salinity and temperature is a complicated non-linear one and no simple formula has been devised for it. In practice, values of $\sigma_t$ are obtained from a nomogram or tables which are entered with the appropriate values of salinity and temperature. (Values for $\sigma_t$ are quoted without units because specific gravity is actually used in the definition rather than density.)

The reason why one can omit the pressure terms of $\sigma_{s,t,p}$ is because in synoptic oceanography one is usually comparing water masses at the same depth (i.e. the same pressure) or over the same range of depth. However, it should be noted that the effect of pressure on density is not negligible. For instance, a sample of water of salinity 35‰ and temperature 0°C would have a $\sigma_{s,t,p}$ at the surface (i.e. $\sigma_t$) of 28·13 but at a depth of 4000m it would be increased by compression to 48·49.

Associated with the change of density with pressure (compressibility) is a change of temperature if the water does not exchange heat with its surroundings (adiabatic change). For instance, if water of salinity 35‰ and temperature 5·00°C were lowered adiabatically to a depth of 4000 m its temperature would increase to 5·45°C due to compression. Conversely, if its temperature were 5·00°C at 4000m depth and it were raised adiabatically to the surface it would cool to 4·56°C due to expansion. This effect has to be considered when water is changing depth significantly. In the example above the temperature of 5·00°C at 4000m depth is called the *"in situ"* temperature while 4·56°C is called the "potential" temperature. The use of potential temperature is discussed with an example in Chapter 4. The density of a water sample appropriate to its salinity and potential temperature is called its "potential" density.

The *specific volume* is the reciprocal of density and for some purposes it is more useful. One application is in the calculation of currents from the distribution of mass as is described in *Dynamical Oceanography*. The specific volume *in situ* is written as $\alpha_{s,t,p}$; for convenience a specific volume anomaly $\delta$ is defined as:

$$\delta = \alpha_{s,t,p} - \alpha_{35,0,p}.$$

The last quantity is the specific volume of an arbitrary standard sea-water of salinity 35‰ and temperature 0°C at the pressure $p$. This standard was chosen so that $\delta$ is usually positive. Again the connection between $\alpha$ or $\delta$ and salinity, temperature and pressure is complicated. The values of $\alpha_{35,0,p}$ are tabulated for all practical values of $p$. For $\delta$, Bjerknes and Sandström examined the experimental values as functions of salinity, temperature and pressure and showed that $\delta$ could be broken down into components as:

$$\delta = \delta_s + \delta_t + \delta_{s,t} + \delta_{s,p} + \delta_{t,p} + \delta_{s,t,p}$$

where $\delta_s$ represents the main effect of salinity, $\delta_{s,t}$ represents the interacting effect of salinity and temperature, etc. In practice, the last term is small enough to be ignored, while the two pressure terms, $\delta_{s,p}$ and $\delta_{t,p}$ are smaller than the first three terms. In fact, Montgomery and Wooster pointed out that in the actual oceans the sum of the first three terms, $\delta_s + \delta_t + \delta_{s,t} = \delta_T$, is adequate in most practical cases to describe the specific volume of water masses. They proposed calling this term, $\delta_T$, the *thermosteric anomaly* and in recent years it has come to be used frequently in place of $\sigma_t$ to describe the density of ocean water. The physical units for $\alpha$, the $\delta$'s and $\delta_T$ are cm³/g. Numerical values for $\delta_T$ may be 50 to

$100 \times 10^{-5}$ cm³/g; for $\delta_{s,p}$ or $\delta_{t,p}$ they are usually of the order of only 5 to $15 \times 10^{-5}$ cm³/g/1000 m depth. To avoid having to write the $10^{-5}$ in the numerical values, it is the practice to express these quantities in centilitres per ton, i.e. units of 1 cl ( = 10 ml) per metric ton of 1000 kg, the small difference between the litre and 1000 cm³ being disregarded. The above values for $\delta_T$ would then be written as 50 to 100 cl/ton.

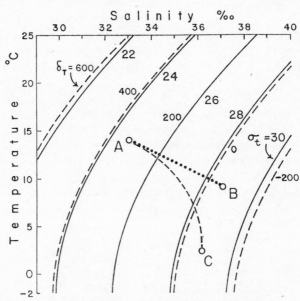

FIG. 2. *Temperature/salinity plotting sheet showing isopleths of density ($\sigma_t$) and of thermosteric anomaly $\delta_T$.*

The shape of the $\sigma_t$ and $\delta_T$ curves with temperature and salinity may be seen in the temperature/salinity plotting sheet of Fig. 2. It is worth noting that the slope of the lines of constant $\sigma_t$ and $\delta_T$ ("isopleths" of $\sigma_t$ and $\delta_T$) changes markedly with temperature. Taking the isopleth of $\sigma_t = 26$ as an example, as it goes from higher to lower temperature the curve becomes more nearly parallel to the temperature axis. This means that at the low temperatures which occur in polar regions, change of temperature is less effective in changing density than is change of salinity, in contrast to the situation at higher temperatures (in low latitudes) where temperature is more effective. Isopleths of thermosteric anomaly $\delta_T$ run substantially parallel to those of $\sigma_t$ but the values change in the opposite direction. The density of a large proportion of the waters of the oceans lies between $\sigma_t = 25 \cdot 5 - 28 \cdot 5$ which corresponds approximately to $\delta_T = 250$ to $-50$.

The tables from which values of $\sigma_t$ or $\delta_T$ are obtained are based upon laboratory determinations of density at different temperatures and salinities. These basic data have been reviewed by Eckart who points out that the accuracy of the laboratory data is limited and is such that the fourth figure, i.e. that in the second decimal place, in $\sigma_t$ is meaningless, and that the figure in the first decimal place is uncertain to $\pm 2$ units. (i.e. the accuracy in density is about $\pm 2$ in $10^4$). These remarks apply to the absolute values of $\sigma_t$. Fortunately the oceanographer is not often concerned with absolute values but more with comparative ones, or differences, which are considered to be more accurate than the absolute values. The oceanographer therefore continues to quote values of $\sigma_t$ to two decimal places, i.e. usually to four significant figures. One of the advantages of the thermosteric anomaly ($\delta_T$) is that it is adequately expressed by only three significant figures. The fact that $\sigma_t$ is expressed to four significant figures does not present an inconsistency because the first figure (i.e. 2) in the value of $\sigma_t$ is always the same in ocean waters below the surface.

One reason why temperature and salinity and hence density are important identifying properties of sea-water is because they are "conservative properties" away from the surface. That is to say, below the surface there is no significant process by which either quantity is changed except by mixing. Near the surface, evaporation or precipitation may change salinity, while many processes may change the temperature, as discussed in Chapter 5.

## OTHER CHARACTERISTICS

Other characteristics of sea-water which are of some help in identifying particular water masses are the dissolved oxygen content, concentration of phosphate or silicate ion, plankton, silt, etc. These, however, have to be used with care because they are not conservative.   Biological processes may change the concentration of oxygen without any movement of the water mass, silt may settle out etc. These other constituents generally occur in such small concentrations that their variation does not significantly affect the density nor does it affect the relations between chlorinity, salinity and conductivity.

One of the physical characteristics of sea-water which has recently been redetermined is the specific heat.   Cox and Smith of the National Institute of Oceanography have shown that the earlier and only previous data available (measured in 1889) are significantly in error.   The new values are estimated to be accurate to $\pm 0.05\%$ and are 1 to 2% higher than the old ones.   There is a marked variation in specific heat with variation in salinity and also a variation with temperature.

Some of the other thermal properties of sea-water and of sea-ice are described in Chapter 7 in the section on "Ice in the Sea".

## COLOUR OF SEA-WATER

A number of investigators have considered the reasons for the colour of the sea which ranges from deep blue to green or even greenish-yellow.   The number of records of sea colour is not great but broadly speaking the deep or indigo blue colour is characteristic of tropical and equatorial seas, particularly where there is little biological production.    At higher latitudes the colour changes through green-blue to green in polar regions.   Coastal waters are generally greenish.   It is certain that there is no one explanation for all the colours seen. In low latitudes where the water is clear and lacks particulate matter, it is considered that selective molecular scattering of sunlight is responsible for the blue colour of the sea as it is for the blue of the sky. Where particulate matter is present, especially phytoplankton (small floating plants), there is less transmission, more scattering by the particles, and probably absorption by soluble organic substances produced by the plankton. In some coastal regions, rivers bring in dissolved organic substances which emphasize the yellowish-green colour. In other regions, rivers bring in finely divided inorganic material, mud and silt, which may impart their own colour to the water by reflection from the particles. In fjords fed by rivers from glaciers, the surface low-salinity layer may be a milky white from the finely divided "rock flour" produced by abrasion in the glaciers and carried down by the rivers. The material may be kept in suspension by turbulence in the upper layer for a time but when it sinks into the saline water below it flocculates and sinks more rapidly. When diving in such a region one may be able to see only a fraction of a metre in the upper layer but be able to see several metres in the saline water below. The colour of sea-water can be judged most conveniently against the white Secchi disc (Chapter 6) as it is lowered to determine the transparency of the water.


## SOUND IN THE SEA

In the atmosphere man receives much of his information about the material world by means of wave energy, either electromagnetic (light) or mechanical (sound). Light in the visible part of the spectrum is attenuated less than sound in the atmosphere, but in the sea the reverse is the case. In clear ocean water, sunlight may be detectable down to 1000m but the range at which man can see details of objects in the sea is rarely more than 50m and usually less. Being denied the use of his eyes in the sea, except for close range when diving, man has made much use of sound waves to obtain information. With echo sounders the depth to the bottom may be measured up to the maximum in the ocean. With sonar the distance and direction of a submarine may be determined up to ranges of a few hundred metres and of fish to somewhat lesser ranges. Conditions in the sea are such that image formation by sound waves is impracticable.

The speed of sound (longitudinal waves) in water is given by the relation $V = \sqrt{E/\rho}$ where $E$ is the adiabatic compressibility and $\rho$ is density. As these quantities depend on temperature, salinity and pressure so does the speed. The speed of sound at a salinity of 34·85‰ (deep-water average) and 0°C is 1445 m/sec. It increases by approximately 4 m/sec per C deg rise of temperature, by 1·5 m/sec per 1‰ increase in salinity and by 18 m/sec per 1000 m increase in depth. Since the speed, wavelength ($\lambda$) and frequency ($n$) are connected by the wave equation $V = \lambda n$, the wavelength for a frequency of 10 kilocycles/sec is about 14 cm and for a frequency of 100 kc/sec is about 1·4 cm. Most echo sounders and sonars operate at frequencies in this range. The speed does not depend on frequency.

Since the size of the sound source of an echo sounder is not much larger than the wavelength, the angular width of the sound beam emitted is large. With a 12 kc/sec echo sounder the beam width in which the energy is no less than one half of its maximum will be of the order of 30° to 60°, which means that it is difficult to distinguish details of the bottom topography. It is possible to improve the resolution by using higher frequencies of 100 or even 200 kc/sec but as the absorption of sea-water for sound energy increases with the square of the frequency, this may entail loss of range or depth of water which can be penetrated.

In echo sounding applications, the sound energy is directed vertically downward and the only effect of change of water properties is to modify the speed of sound and so introduce an error when determining the depth from the formula: depth $= \frac{1}{2}tV$ where $t$ is the time taken for a sound pulse to travel from the ship to the sea bottom and back. In open ocean areas the speed of sound varies with depth over a range of a few tens of metres per second and for echo sounding purposes an average is used, with corrections determined by the water properties if accurate depths are needed.

The fact that the speed depends on the water properties also means that refraction occurs, i.e. the direction of travel of the sound waves may be altered by the changes or inhomogeneities in the water properties which are characteristic of the sea. Small scale inhomogeneities give rise to changes in direction of neighbouring sound waves and are a basic reason why it is difficult to form images by sound waves in the sea. The effect is the same as occurs when one looks at an object through the hot air rising over a fire or emerging from the tail pipe of an aircraft jet engine. When the source of sound is near the surface, as is the case with ship's sonar equipment, the temperature structure of the upper water is very important in its effect on the direction of propagation of the sound waves. The various possibilities are too numerous to discuss here. On a larger scale, the distribution of properties with depth in the sea is often such as to give rise to a sound speed minimum at about 1000 m depth with higher values above and below. Sound waves which start in the neighbourhood of this depth tend to stay there because sound energy which is directed above or below the horizontal tends to be refracted back into the horizontal. This situation is referred to as a "sound channel"; low frequency sound (hundreds of cycles per second) may be detected after travelling thousands of miles in it.

Since the ratio of the speed of sound in water to that in air (about 4·5 to 1) is large, only a small amount of the sound energy starting in one medium will penetrate through the interface into the other, in contrast to the relative efficiency of passage of light energy through the water/air interface (speed ratio only 1·33 to 1). This is the reason why a man standing on the shore, or even with his head under water (but his ears not full of water), is unaware of the noises in the sea, and why it is not possible to speak directly from the air to a diver under water. However, it is possible to design mechanical transducers, such as hydrophones or echo sounder sources, to pick up sound energy from the water or transmit it into the water efficiently.

# CHAPTER FOUR

# Typical Distributions of Water Characteristics in the Oceans

IN THE previous chapter attention was drawn to temperature and salinity as ocean water characteristics. These quantities vary from place to place in the ocean, and from their distribution we can learn a good deal about the average circulation of the waters. In this chapter, some of the typical distributions will be described so that the reader may gain some feeling for them and be able to recognize normal and abnormal distributions.

A salient feature of the distribution of many water characteristics is that they are horizontally stratified or nearly so. In other words, the sea is made up of layers as far as these characteristics are concerned, and horizontal changes are much smaller than vertical ones in the same distance. For instance, near the equator the temperature of the water may drop from 25°C at the surface to 5°C at a depth of 1 km, but it may be necessary to go 5000 km north or south from the equator to reach a latitude where the surface temperature has fallen to 5°C. The average vertical temperature gradient (change of temperature per unit distance) in this case is about 5000 times the horizontal one. However, the horizontal variations do exist and therefore the water properties are distributed in three dimensions. This makes it difficult to display them when we are limited to plotting on paper which has only two dimensions. We are usually forced to represent a single real three-dimensional distribution by a number of two-dimensional ones, such as vertical and horizontal sections.

To appreciate the way in which our understanding of these distributions is built up, it is helpful to describe briefly how the data are collected. The oceanographer goes to sea for a cruise in a research ship (Pl. 1) to "occupy a number of oceanographic stations" (sometimes called "hydrographic stations"). This means that at a number of pre-selected locations ("stations") the ship is stopped and the oceanographers measure the water properties from surface to deep water. For each station the measurements are plotted as "vertical profiles" or graphs of depth against temperature, salinity, etc. The vertical profiles from stations along a line may then be put together to form a "vertical section" of water properties, or the data from a selected depth may be plotted and contoured to show the horizontal distribution of the property at that depth in the same way that a contour map of land shows the distribution of height over an area. These are the synopses of the spatial distributions of the data.

After the field work and the subsequent plotting of the data, the really interesting part starts. The oceanographer sits down with the plots before him to try to determine the reasons why they are as they are. Among the processes which may be acting are horizontal flow, mixing, diffusion, heat flow through the surface, etc. There is no set routine method that will solve all problems. The oceanographer does exactly what a detective does in trying to solve a crime. Each assembles all the data (clues) that he can and then tries to deduce from them what really happened. Each may have all the clues needed, or may lack vital ones, or may be looking at the wrong ones. The oceanographer perhaps has one advantage over the detective. He can often go back to make more observations, whereas the criminal may not be so obliging as to keep repeating his crime.

There is one more dimension to be considered. In addition to the spatial variations of properties (vertical and horizontal) there may be variations in time ("temporal" variations). To observe these the oceanographic ship occupies an "anchor station", i.e. anchors for a day, a week or longer, or else returns to the same station time after time, to measure the water properties there. The data are plotted as "time series" in various ways to see if there are daily ("diurnal") or seasonal variations. Generally the diurnal variations are only appreciable to depths of a few metres and seasonal ones to 100 to 300 m. At greater depths variations take place only over periods of years or possibly even centuries.

Before giving descriptions of some of the typical distributions of water properties, the following statistics on ocean water temperatures and salinities are given for general information:

(a) 75% of the total volume of the ocean water has properties within the range from 0° to 6°C in temperature and 34 to 35‰ in salinity,

(b) 50% of the total volume of the oceans has properties between 1·3° and 3·8°C and between 34·6‰ and 34·8‰,

(c) the mean temperature of the world ocean is 3·5°C and the mean salinity is 34·7‰.

One feature which will be noted about the spatial distribution of water properties is that in the surface and upper waters there is a distinct tendency for the arrangement of some of them to be "zonal", i.e. the value of a property may be much the same across the ocean in the east-west direction but may change rapidly in the north-south direction. As a consequence, when describing ocean water property distributions we frequently wish to refer to the position of an ocean area in terms of its north-south position even when we do not need to state the latitude explicitly. When doing so, the adjective "equatorial" refers to the zone near to the equator, while the adjective "tropical" refers to zones near the tropics ($23\frac{1}{2}$° N or S of the equator). The distinction between "equatorial" and "tropical" should be noted as it is often significant; when the two are to be lumped together the term "low latitude" will be used, in contrast to the "high latitudes" which are near to the poles, north and south. "Subtropical" refers to zones on the high latitude side of the tropical zones. The term "polar" is properly applied in oceanography only to the Arctic region but is often used of the ocean close to Antarctica.

## DENSITY DISTRIBUTION

The distribution of the density of sea-water at the ocean surface can be described roughly by stating that the value of $\sigma_t$ increases from about 22 near the equator to 26 to 27 at 50° to 60° latitude, and beyond this it decreases slightly (Fig. 3).

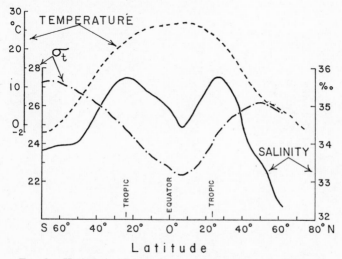

FIG. 3.  *Variation with latitude of surface temperature, salinity and density* ($\sigma_t$)—*average for all oceans.*

More important, however, is the distribution of density in the vertical direction.  A guiding principle here is that the density normally increases as depth increases.  This is simply a consequence of the general tendency in Nature for a system to settle down in a state of minimum energy.  This is the case in still water when the least dense water is at the surface and the most dense at the bottom. The density in the sea does not increase uniformly with depth however.  In equatorial and tropical regions there is usually a shallow surface-zone of nearly uniform density, then a zone where the density increases rapidly with depth and below this the deep zone where the density increases more slowly with depth (Fig. 4). There is little variation with latitude of the deep water $\sigma_t$ which is about 27·9. In consequence, in high latitudes where the surface $\sigma_t$ rises to 27 or more there is a much smaller increase of density with depth than in low latitudes and the intermediate zone of rapid increase is less evident.

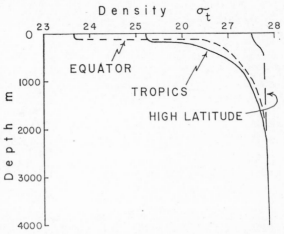

FIG. 4. *Typical density/depth profiles at low and high latitudes.*

The rate of change of the density with depth determines the water's *stability* or unwillingness to move vertically. Where the stability is high, vertical movement and vertical mixing are minimized. Where there is no change of potential density with depth the water has neutral stability and can be mixed vertically with no effort. Situations in which the potential density decreases with increase of depth represent unstable conditions and are uncommon below the surface layer. In the surface layer (to 50 or 100 m) slight instability often occurs in mid-latitudes, possibly due to increases in salinity resulting from evaporation.

The water in the depth zone where density is increasing rapidly with depth (called the "pycnocline") is very stable. That is to say, it takes much more energy to displace it up or down than in a region where density changes slowly with depth. A result is that turbulence, which causes most of the mixing between different water bodies, is unable to penetrate through this stable layer. The pycnocline then, although it is too slight to offer any barrier to the sinking of bodies which are much denser than water, offers a real barrier to the passage of water and water properties in the vertical direction, either up or down.

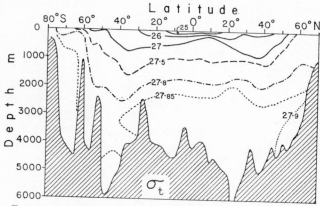

FIG. 5.   *Density ($\sigma_t$) in a south–north section of the western Atlantic (after Wüst).*

Perhaps the most illuminating graphical presentation of the distribution of density is a north–south vertical section through the ocean, such as Fig. 5, showing isopleths of $\sigma_t$. Those in the upper layers tend to be concave upward, showing the increase from equator to pole. Below about 2000 m however, the total range of values of $\sigma_t$ is only from about 27·8 to 27·9.

A further point to bear in mind when considering the ocean circulations later is that there is a strong tendency for flow to be along surfaces of constant potential density. For most practical purposes we can regard this as to be along surfaces of constant $\sigma_t$.

For instance, the processes which give ocean waters their particular properties act almost exclusively at the surface, and one can trace the origin of even the deepest water back to a region of formation at the surface somewhere. Since deep ocean water is of high density this implies that it must have been formed at high latitudes because only there is high density water found at the surface. After formation it sinks along constant density surfaces. When the word "sink" is used here it does not necessarily imply that the water goes straight down like a stone. The sinking is often combined with horizontal motion so that the water actually moves in a direction only slightly inclined below the horizontal. The slopes of the constant density surfaces in Fig. 5 are exaggerated because of the vertical scale exaggeration used in plotting the data.

In the open ocean most of the variations of density are due to variations of temperature. Only in certain ocean areas, such as the north-east Pacific and the polar regions, does the variation in salinity play a significant part. In coastal waters, fjords and estuaries, on the other hand, the salinity is often the controlling factor in determining density, while temperature is of secondary importance.


## TEMPERATURE DISTRIBUTION

The distribution of temperature at the surface of the open ocean is approximately zonal, the lines of constant temperature ('isotherms') running roughly east-west (Figs. 6 and 7). (The purpose of the projection in this and some subsequent figures is to show the ocean with the areas between the parallels of latitude being reasonably correct, rather than being grossly exaggerated at high latitudes as they are on a Mercator's projection.) Near the coast where currents are diverted the isotherms may swing more nearly north and south. Also, along the eastern boundaries of the oceans low surface temperatures often occur due to upwelling of subsurface cool water, e.g. along the west coast of North America in summer (Fig. 6). The open ocean surface temperature decreases from values as high as 28°C just north of the equator to nearly −2°C near ice at high latitudes both north and south. Values for the surface temperature from south to north for all the oceans averaged together are shown in Fig. 3.

Below the surface the water can usually be divided into three zones in terms of its temperature structure (Fig. 8). There is an upper zone of 50 to 200 m depth with temperatures similar to those at the surface, a zone below this extending from 500 to 1000 m in which the temperature decreases rapidly, and a deep zone in which the temperature decreases more slowly. Typical temperatures at low latitudes would be 20°C at the surface, 8°C at 500 m, 5°C at 1000 m and 2°C at 4000 m.

The depth at which the temperature gradient (rate of decrease of temperature with increasing depth) is a maximum is called the *thermocline*. With actual observations of temperature in the sea it is sometimes difficult to determine this depth accurately because of minor irregularities in the temperature/depth profile and it is easier to pick out a "thermocline zone" as a range of depth over which the temperature gradient is large compared to that above and below. Even for the "zone", it is often hard to define precisely the depth limits, particularly the lower limit, and one must accept some degree of approximation in stating the depth limits of the thermocline zone. However, in low and middle latitudes it is clear that there is a thermocline present all the time at depths between 200 and 1000 m. This is referred to as the "main" or "permanent" thermocline. In polar waters there is no permanent thermocline.

The temperature in the upper zone shows seasonal variations, particularly in middle latitudes. The layer between the surface and a depth of 25 to 200 m is usually at much the same temperature as the surface water because of mixing due to wind waves. For this reason it is referred to as the "mixed layer" (Fig. 8). In winter the surface temperature is low and the mixed layer is deep and may extend to the main thermocline. In summer the surface temperature rises and a "seasonal" thermocline often develops in the upper zone (Fig. 8). The thermocline zones are of high stability

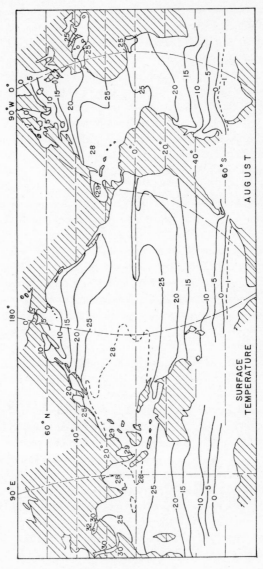

Fig. 6. *Surface temperature of the oceans in August.*

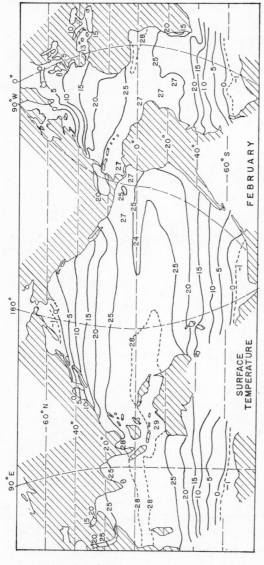

FIG. 7.  *Surface temperature of the oceans in February.*

and for this reason they separate the waters of the upper from those of the deep zones.

An illustration of the growth and decay of the seasonal thermocline is shown in Fig. 9a. This figure shows monthly temperature profiles from March 1956 to January 1957 taken at Ocean Weather Station "P" in the eastern North Pacific. From March to August the temperature gradually increases due to absorption of solar energy. A mixed layer from the surface down to 30m or more is evident

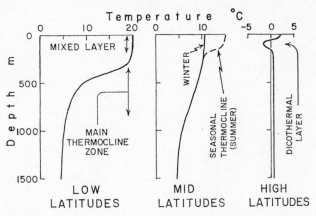

Fig. 8. *Typical mean temperature profiles in the open ocean.*

all the time. After August there is a net loss of heat energy from the sea while continued wind mixing erodes away the seasonal thermocline until the isothermal condition of March is approached again.

The same data may be presented in alternative forms. In Fig. 9b is given a time series plot showing the depth of the isotherms during the year. (The original data includes the alternate months which were omitted from Fig. 9a to avoid crowding.) In Fig. 9c are plotted the temperatures at selected depths, "isobaths" of temperature. The different forms in which the thermocline appears in these three presentations should be noted. In Fig. 9a it appears

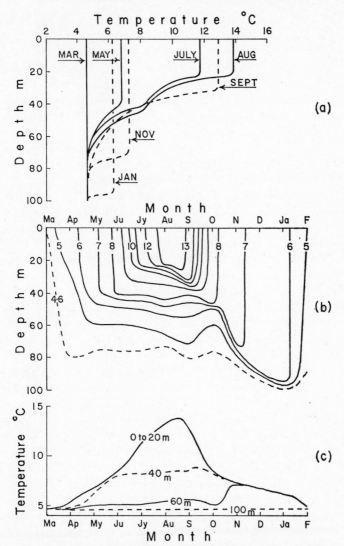

FIG. 9.  *Growth and decay of the seasonal thermocline at 50° N, 145° W in the eastern North Pacific (Pacific Oceanographic Group, Canada).*

as a maximum gradient region in the temperature/depth graphs, and in July and August there are really two thermocline zones. In Fig. 9b the thermocline appears as a crowding of the isotherms which rises from about 50 m in May to 30 m in August and then descends to 100 m in January. In Fig. 9c the thermocline appears as a wide separation of the 20 m and 60 m isobaths between May and October, and between the 60 m and 100 m isobaths after that as the thermocline descends.

At high latitudes the surface temperatures are much lower than at lower latitudes, while the deep water temperatures are little different. In consequence the main thermocline may not be present and only a seasonal thermocline may occur. In high northern latitudes there is often a "dicothermal" layer at 50 to 100 m (Fig. 8). This is a layer of cold water, down to −1·6°C, sandwiched between the warmer surface and the deeper waters.

Diurnal *temperature variations* at the surface are small in the open oceans (rarely more than 0·3C°) but may be larger (2 to 3C°) in sheltered and shallow water near the coast. The smallness of the change is partly because there is usually some mixing of the warmed surface water with cooler subsurface water. A more important factor is that most of the daily heat input from solar radiation is used to evaporate water, leaving only a part available for raising the water temperature. Diurnal variations extend only to a depth of a few metres. Annual variations in temperature (compare Figs. 6 and 7) at the surface rise from 2C° at the equator to 8C° at 40° latitude and then decrease toward the polar regions (due to the heat required in the melting or freezing processes where sea-ice occurs). Near the coast, larger annual variations (10 to 15C°) may occur in sheltered areas. These annual variations in temperature get progressively less with depth and are rarely perceptible below 100 to 300 m. The maximum temperature at the surface occurs in August/ September in the northern hemisphere and the minimum during February/March. Below the surface the times of occurrence of the maxima and minima are delayed by as much as two months relative to the times at the surface.

These statements about annual variations in temperature are made on the basis of observations at fixed stations. Defant has pointed out that in most oceanic regions the surface water is moving and therefore the statements about annual variations at fixed stations refer not to a particular body of water but to a continually changing one. For a region where the ocean currents are zonal, i.e. east–west, there will be little difference between the annual variation at a fixed station and that in a body of water moving with the current. But in a region where the flow is north–south this will not be the case because of the difference in annual mean temperature and of annual variation in the north–south direction. For a planktonic organism which drifts with the water it is the variation in the individual water mass which is important. Little attention seems to have been paid by oceanographers to determining the annual change of temperature (or other properties) appropriate to an individual moving water mass.

A reference was made earlier to *upwelling* which occurs seasonally along the eastern shores of the oceans. It takes place when the wind blows towards the equator along the coast. The frictional stress of the wind on the water combined with the effect of the rotation of the earth causes water in the surface layer to move away from the shore. It is replaced by water which "upwells" from below the surface. Since the water temperature decreases as depth increases in these regions, the upwelled water is cooler than the original surface water and a characteristic band of low temperatures develops close to the coast. This may be seen off the Pacific coast of North America in Fig. 6 and off the Atlantic coast of South Africa in Fig. 7. Often the upwelled water also has greater concentrations of nutrients (phosphates, nitrates, silicates, etc.) than the original surface water which had been depleted by biological demands. The result is that upwelling is important in replenishing the surface layers with these components which are needed for biological production.

It is important to note that the water which upwells is not deep water. Comparison of the properties of the upwelled water with those in the water column before the start of upwelling has shown that the water comes to the surface from depths which are usually between 50 and 300 m. It was for this reason that the earlier reference was to the upwelling of "subsurface" water only.

In the deep water below the thermocline zone the temperature generally decreases as depth increases to about 4000 m, the average depth of the world oceans. In the deep trenches, however, the *in situ* temperature often increases slowly with depth beyond 3000 to 4000 m due to the effect of increasing pressure (see Chapter 3). When considering oceanic situations where considerable changes of depth of water masses occur, it is best to plot potential temperature in order to eliminate the effect of change of depth (i.e. pressure) which appears in the *in situ* temperature. An excellent example is shown in the data of Table 1 taken from the results of the Dutch *Snellius* Expedition.

TABLE 1

*Comparison of* in situ *and potential temperatures etc. in the Mindanao Trench near the Philippine Islands.*

| Depth (m) | Salinity (‰) | Temperature in situ (°C) | Temperature Potential (°C) | Density $\sigma_t$ | Density Potential |
|---|---|---|---|---|---|
| 1455 | 34·58 | 3·20 | 3·09 | 27·55 | 27·56 |
| 2470 | 34·64 | 1·82 | 1·65 | 27·72 | 27·73 |
| 3470 | 34·67 | 1·59 | 1·31 | 27·76 | 27·78 |
| 4450 | 34·67 | 1·65 | 1·25 | 27·76 | 27·78 |
| 6450 | 34·67 | 1·93 | 1·25 | 27·74 | 27·79 |
| 8450 | 34·69 | 2·23 | 1·22 | 27·72 | 27·79 |
| 10035 | 34·67 | 2·48 | 1·16 | 27·69 | 27·79 |

It is seen that while the *in situ* temperature reaches a minimum at 3470 m and thereafter increases, the potential temperature decreases to the bottom. The salinity values show the small change in this characteristic. The density values show that $\sigma_t$ decreases as depth increases from 4450 m, giving the appearance of instability. However, the potential density increases to 6450 m and then remains constant showing that when the adiabatic compression with increase of depth is taken into account the water is not unstable but in neutral equilibrium below 6450 m.

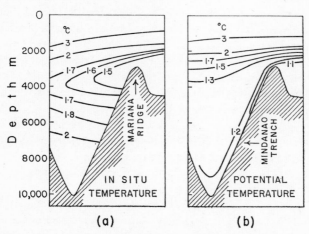

Fig. 10.  In situ *and potential temperature distributions in the Mindanao Trench (after van Riel).*

The effect of the correction from *in situ* to potential temperature is more dramatically shown in Fig. 10 from the Expedition Report. The plot of the *in situ* temperature section (Fig. 10a) would suggest a flow of cool water over the sill, continuing to descend slowly across the Trench but staying near mid-depth and leaving warmer bottom water undisturbed. The plot of potential temperature (Fig. 10b) shows a very different pattern with the water which passes over the sill in reality flowing down the slope to the bottom of the Trench.

## SALINITY DISTRIBUTION

The salinity of the surface waters is basically zonal in distribution (Fig. 11) although not as clearly as the temperature. The average surface salinity distribution (Fig. 3) is different from that for temperature in that it has a minimum just north of the equator and maximum values in the sub-tropics at about 25° N and S of the equator. The minimum and maxima are evident in the individual oceans in Fig. 11. Values decrease toward high latitudes. Observations make it clear that surface salinity is determined by the opposing effects of evaporation increasing it and precipitation decreasing it. The salinity maxima are in the trade wind regions where the annual evaporation is greater than precipitation.

It will be noted from Fig. 3 that the density of the surface water has a single minimum at low latitudes, corresponding to the single temperature maximum. The salinity does exert some influence on density but not sufficient for the tropical maxima to appear on the $\sigma_t$ curve as density maxima.

The range of surface salinity values in the open ocean is from 33 to 37‰. Lower values occur locally near coasts where large rivers empty and in the polar regions where ice melts. Higher values occur in regions of high evaporation such as the eastern Mediterranean (39‰) and the Red Sea (41‰). On the average the North Atlantic is the most saline ocean at the surface (35·5‰), the South Atlantic and South Pacific less so (about 35·2‰) and the North Pacific the least saline (34·2‰).

The salinity distribution in the vertical direction cannot be summarized quite as simply as the temperature distribution. In the upper water the reason for this is that density, which is the factor determining the stable position of a water body in the vertical direction, is determined chiefly by temperature in the open ocean (except in the polar seas). Therefore, water of higher temperature (lower density) is generally found in the upper layers and water of lower temperature (higher density) in the deeper layers. The

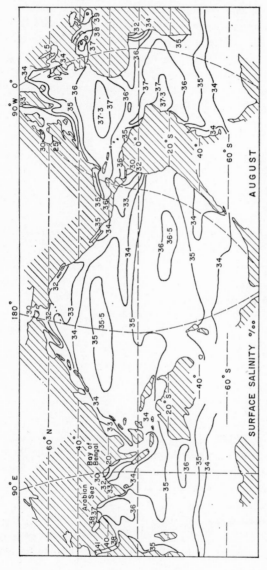

FIG. 11. *Surface salinity of the oceans in August.*

variations in salinity which occur in open ocean waters are usually not sufficient in their effect upon density to override the effect of temperature. Therefore it is quite possible to have either high or low salinity in the warmer surface and upper layers.

In the vertical direction in the equatorial, tropical and subtropical regions there is a marked salinity minimum at 600 to 1000 m (Fig. 12) with the salinity then increasing to 2000 m. In the Atlantic it decreases

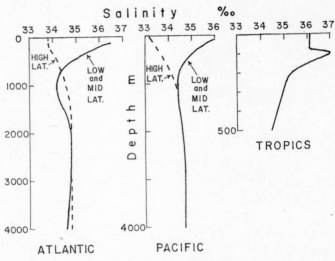

FIG. 12. *Typical mean salinity profiles in the open ocean.*

slightly below this. In the tropics there is often a sharp salinity maximum at about 100 m depth close to the top of the thermocline. In high latitudes, where the surface value is low, the salinity generally increases with depth to about 2000 m, with no subsurface minimum.

In the deep waters, 4000 m and deeper, the salinity is relatively uniform at 34·6 to 34·9‰ through the world ocean. Remembering that the deep water temperature also has only a small range (−0·9°

to 2°C) this means that the deep water environment is very uniform in character.

Information on temporal *variations of salinity* is much less than for temperature which is more easily measured. Annual variations of salinity in the open ocean are probably generally less than 0·5‰. In regions of marked annual variation in precipitation, such as the eastern North Pacific and the Bay of Bengal and near ice, there are large annual variations. These variations are confined to the surface layers because in such regions the effect of reduced salinity may override the effect of temperature in reducing the sea-water density. This keeps the low salinity water in the surface layer. Diurnal variations of salinity appear to be very small.


## DISSOLVED OXYGEN DISTRIBUTION

In addition to the solids dissolved in sea-water there are also gases. One which has been widely used as a water characteristic is oxygen, expressed as the number of millilitres of oxygen gas at NTP dissolved in one litre of sea-water. The range of values found in the sea is from 0 to 8 ml/l, but a large proportion of values fall within the more limited range from 1 to 6 ml/l. The atmosphere is the main source of oxygen dissolved in sea-water and at the surface the water is usually very close to being saturated. Sometimes, in the upper 10 to 20 m, the water is supersaturated with the oxygen which is a by-product of photosynthesis by marine plants. Below the surface layers the water is usually less than saturated because oxygen is consumed by living organisms and by the oxidation of detritus. Low values of dissolved oxygen in sea-water may often be taken to indicate that the water has been away from the surface for a long time, the oxygen having been depleted by the biological and detrital demands. The deep water in the North Pacific has a much smaller dissolved oxygen content than Atlantic water (compare Figs. 23 and 29); this is taken to indicate that this water has been away from the surface for a greater period of time and that the deep water circulation may be slower in the Pacific. In particular regions, such as the Black Sea and the Cariaco Trench (in the Caribbean), there is no oxygen and even hydrogen sulphide is present instead. This indicates that the water has been stagnant there for a long time.

A conspicuous feature of the oxygen distribution in the vertical direction in the open ocean is the occurrence of minimum values in the upper 1000 m below the surface layer. This minimum is particularly evident in the equatorial Atlantic and in the eastern Pacific extending west from the Gulf of Panama (Figs. 23 and 29). Suggestions for the cause of this minimum are basically either that this intermediate water is in a region of minimal motion so that there is little circulation or mixing to refresh the water and replace the oxygen consumed, or that biological detritus accumulates in this region because of the increase in density with depth and uses up the oxygen. Neither suggestion is accepted as satisfactory in itself and the oxygen minimum still requires a full explanation. As the production and utilization of oxygen are essentially biochemical matters they will not be pursued further here but it must be remembered that whenever oxygen content is considered as a water property it must be used with caution since it is non-conservative.

CHAPTER FIVE

# Water, Salt and Heat Budgets of the Oceans

IN THE basic sciences much use is made of a number of conservation principles, conservation of energy, of momentum etc., and these rather simple principles have very far reaching results and valuable applications. Conservation of heat energy as applied to the oceans will be discussed later in this chapter. First we will discuss two other principles, the second of which is peculiar to oceanography. They are the conservation of volume and the conservation of salt.

## CONSERVATION OF VOLUME

The principle of conservation of volume (or the equation of continuity as it is sometimes called) follows from the fact that the compressibility of water is small. It says that if water is flowing into a closed full container at a certain rate it must be flowing out somewhere else at the same rate. "Containers" such as bays, fjords, etc., in the oceans are not closed in the sense that they have lids on, but if one observes that the mean sea level in a bay remains constant (i.e. after averaging out the tides) then there is no flow through the upper surface and the bay is equivalent to a closed container. One might say that this principle is just commonsense. This may be true but nonetheless it is science too. It may lead to interesting results. For example, many of the fjords of Norway or of the British Columbia coast of Canada have large rivers flowing into their inland ends, but on the average the mean sea level in them remains constant. We conclude from the principle of continuity of volume that there must be a simultaneous outflow elsewhere. The only likely place is at the seaward end, and if we measure the currents there we find that in fact there is a net outflow in the surface layer. The direction is correct to balance the inflow from the river but when we check we find that there is a much greater volume flowing out to the sea in this surface layer than in from the river. If conservation of volume is to apply there must be another inflow; the current measurements show that this is from the sea below the outflowing surface layer. The reason for this situation is that the river water being fresh and therefore less dense than the sea-water in the fjord, stays in the surface layers as it flows toward the sea. However, it picks up sea-water from below en route and the outflowing surface layer includes not only the river water but also the extra salt water picked up. The latter is often in much greater volume than the river water, and the surface outflow to the sea is therefore correspondingly greater than the inflow from the river. In addition, the salt water which has been picked up and flushed out of the fjord must be replaced; this is the cause of the subsurface inflow from the sea. The type of circulation described above is nowadays referred to as an "estuarine" one; it will be discussed in more detail in Chapter 8.

In practice when we apply the conservation of volume principle we must also allow for addition of water by precipitation (rain and snow) and loss by evaporation. The practical form of the principle may be stated as: Salt water flow in + River flow + Precipitation = Salt water flow out + Evaporation.

Symbolically:        $V_i + R + P = V_o + E,$

or rearranged slightly as    $V_o - V_i = (R + P) - E = X.$

Here $V$ stands for "volume" transport, a phrase which is used when we express flow in terms of volume per second rather than as linear speed. The second equation simply says that the net volume flow of salt water balances the net volume flow of fresh water.

## CONSERVATION OF SALT

The principle of conservation of salt asserts that the total amount of dissolved salts in the ocean is constant. When one first learns that the rivers of the world contribute to the sea a total of about $3 \times 10^{12}$ kg of dissolved solids per year, the conservation of salt seems to be contradicted. In principle it is, but in practice it is contradicted only to a negligible extent. The total amount of salt in the oceans is about $10^{19}$ kg, and therefore the amount brought in each year by the rivers increases the ocean salinity by about one part in three million per year. But we can only measure the salinity of sea-water to an accuracy of about $\pm 0.003\%_0$, or about 300 parts in three million taking the mean ocean salinity as $35\%_0$. In other words the oceans are increasing in salinity each year by an amount which is three hundred times smaller than our best accuracy of measurement. So for all practical purposes we can assume that the average salinity of the oceans is constant, at least over periods of tens or even hundreds of years.

The principle of conservation of salt has been demonstrated above for the world ocean as a whole. It can also be used for smaller bodies of water. It turns out to be most useful when applied to bodies of water which have only a limited connection with the main ocean, e.g. the Mediterranean Sea, a bay or a fjord. Conservation of salt in such water bodies is sometimes taken for granted, but strictly speaking it should be verified before being used. That is, before we use the principle we should determine from observations that the salinity distribution does not change significantly over the period of study. At the same time, there is nothing to prevent us from assuming the principle in order to draw some deductions. But we must then remember that until conservation of salt has been demonstrated the deductions which depend on it are subject to doubt.

The principle may be expressed symbolically as:

$$V_i . d_i . S_i = V_o . d_o . S_o$$

where $S_i$ and $S_o$ are the salinities respectively of the inflowing and the outflowing sea-water, and $d_i$ and $d_o$ the respective densities. Since the two densities will be the same within 3% at the most (the difference between ocean and fresh water) the $d$'s can in practice be cancelled leaving:

$$V_i . S_i = V_o . S_o.$$

This equation can be combined with the second equation for conservation of volume to give:

$$V_i = X.S_o/(S_i - S_o) \text{ and } V_o = X.S_i/(S_i - S_o).$$

One can draw some qualitative conclusions from these relations. In the first case, if both $S_o$ and $S_i$ are large they must be similar (because there is an upper limit to $S$ in the ocean), therefore $(S_i - S_o)$ must be small and both $S_o/(S_i - S_o)$ and $S_i/(S_i - S_o)$ must be large. Therefore $V_i$ and $V_o$ must be large compared to $X$, the excess of fresh water inflow over evaporation. In the second case, if $S_o$ is much less than $S_i$, then $V_i$ must be small compared to $X$ while $V_o$ will be only slightly greater than $X$. For the same value of $X$ for both, the exchange of water in the first case with the outside will be large, while in the second case the exchange will be small. One might therefore expect that the body of water in the first case would be less likely to be stagnant than that in the second case.

## CONSERVATION OF HEAT ENERGY

It has already been stated that the temperature of the ocean waters varies from place to place and from time to time. Such variations are indications of heat transfer by currents, absorption of solar energy, loss by evaporation, etc. The size and character of the variations of temperature depends on the net rate of heat flow into or out of a water body, and calculations of this quantity are referred to as *heat budget* studies. In what follows, the symbol $Q$ will be used to represent the rate of heat flow measured in langleys per unit time. (One langley (ly) is one gram calorie per square centimetre.) A subscript will be used to distinguish the different components in the heat budget, e.g. $Q_s$ stands for the rate of flow of solar energy through one square centimetre of the sea surface, $Q_v$ stands for the rate of heat inflow due to currents which are usually in the horizontal direction and then $Q_v$ is measured through a vertical area of one square centimetre. The transfer of water properties due to currents is called "advection", to distinguish it from the transfer due to diffusion, and $Q_v$ is called the advective term in the heat budget. The other important terms in the budget are: $Q_b$, the net heat lost by the sea as long-wave radiation to the atmosphere and space; $Q_h$, the heat leaving the sea surface by conduction, and $Q_e$, the heat lost by evaporation. The other sources of heat inflow, such as that from the earth's interior, change of kinetic energy of waves into heat in the surf, heat from chemical or nuclear reactions etc., are small and are neglected. The heat budget for any particular locality can then be stated by the equation:

$$Q_s - Q_b - Q_h - Q_e + Q_v = Q_T$$

where $Q_T$ is the resultant rate of gain or loss of heat of a body of water in that locality.

If $Q_T$ is zero, i.e. the temperature of the body of water is not changing, this does not mean that there is no heat exchange. It simply means that the sum total of the terms on the left hand side of the equation is zero—net inflow equals net outflow, an example of a steady state condition.

If we apply the equation to the world ocean as a whole, $Q_v$ is zero because then all the advective flows are internal and must add up to zero. Also if we average over a whole year or number of years the seasonal changes average out and $Q_T$ becomes zero. The above equation is then simplified and Mosby has calculated average values for the remaining terms as:

$$Q_s = Q_b + Q_h + Q_e,$$

$$320 = 130 + 20 + 170 \text{ langleys per day.}$$

These values give some idea of the average size of the heat budget terms but it must be realized that the actual values at a particular time and place may vary considerably from these averages. $Q_s$ varies very much from winter to summer in high latitudes but less in low latitudes. $Q_h$ and $Q_e$ vary from place to place and with the seasons, and may also change sign, i.e. $Q_h$ may represent heat conducted into the water or out of the water, $Q_e$ may represent heat lost from the water when evaporation occurs or heat gained when condensation of water vapour into the sea occurs. $Q_b$ is the only term which does not vary much with time or place. The reason will be apparent later. The variations in the heat flow terms in different localities give rise to the temperature characterisitics of the regions, and the terms will be discussed individually below.

Before discussing the radiation terms, $Q_s$ and $Q_b$, some aspects of electromagnetic radiation theory will be reviewed briefly. First, Stefan's Law states that all bodies radiate energy at a rate proportional to the fourth power of their absolute temperature ($°K = °C + 273°$). This energy is in the form of electromagnetic radiation with a range or spectrum of wavelengths. Second, the concentration of energy is not the same at all wavelengths but has a marked peak at a wavelength $\lambda_m$ given by Wien's Law; $\lambda_m.T = $ constant, where $T$ is the absolute temperature ($°K$) of the radiating body. For a body at a high temperature the radiant energy is concentrated at short wavelengths and vice versa.

The sun has a surface temperature of some $6000°K$ and radiates energy in all directions at a rate proportional to $6000^4$. According to Wien's Law this energy is concentrated round a wavelength of $0·5\mu$ ($1\mu = 1$ micron $= 10^{-6}$ metre). $50\%$ of the energy is in the visible part of the electromagnetic spectrum (about $0·35$ to $0·7\mu$) while $99\%$ is of wavelength shorter than $4\mu$. This energy is referred to as "short-wave" radiation and is the source of the $Q_s$ term in the heat budget. The "long-wave" radiation term $Q_b$ represents the electromagnetic energy which is radiated outward by the earth (land and sea) at a rate depending on the absolute temperature of the earth. Taking an average temperature of $17°C = 290°K$ for the sea, it is radiating energy at a rate proportional to $290^4$. This is a smaller rate than that for the sun, and as the temperature is lower the wave-length is longer. The wavelength at which the sea radiation reaches its maximum is about $10\,\mu$ (i.e. in the infra-red). 90% of the sea radiation is in the wavelength range from 3 to $80\,\mu$ and this is referred to as "long-wave" radiation in contrast to that from the sun which is chiefly less than $4\,\mu$.

A small fraction of the sun's total radiated energy reaches the earth's atmosphere. Then about 45% of that reaching the atmosphere is lost by scattering back to space, 15% is absorbed in the atmosphere (and helps to maintain its temperature and circulation), and the remaining 40% reaches the land and sea surface. Of the 40% about 25 parts reach the surface as direct radiation from the sun and the remaining 15 come indirectly as scattered radiation from the atmosphere ("sky radiation"). At the sea surface some of the 40% is reflected back to the sky and the remainder ($Q_s$) enters the sea and is absorbed to raise the temperature of the water. The rate at which energy reaches the outside of the atmosphere from the sun is called the "solar constant" and is calculated from measurements from the earth's surface to be about 1·95 ly/min perpendicular to the sun's rays. The 40% which reaches the sea surface then amounts to about 0·8 ly/min when the sun is vertically overhead, or less at other times.

The rate at which *short-wave solar energy* enters the sea, $Q_s$, depends upon a number of factors discussed in the following six paragraphs.

The first factor is the length of the day, i.e. the time that the sun is above the horizon, which varies with the season and the geographic latitude. In the following discussion this factor has been taken into account wherever possible for figures quoted for the heat budget terms, and values given per day are to be understood to refer to a 24 hour period.

The second factor affecting $Q_s$ is absorption in the atmosphere. This depends on the absorption coefficient for short-wave radiation and on the elevation of the sun. The absorption is the combined effect of that due to gas molecules, dust, water vapour, etc. When the sun is vertically overhead, i.e. at an elevation of 90° from the horizontal, the radiation passes through the atmosphere by the shortest possible path and the absorption is a minimum. When the sun is at an elevation of less than 90°, the path of the radiation is greater and the absorption therefore greater.

The elevation of the sun has a second effect. If one considers a beam of radiation from the sun of one square metre cross-section this will cover an area of one square metre of calm sea surface when the sun is vertically overhead at an elevation of 90°. At lower elevations, the beam strikes the sea surface obliquely and is distributed over a larger area than one square metre. The energy density, or amount of energy per square metre of sea surface, therefore decreases as the sun is farther from the vertical. The energy density on the sea surface is proportional to the sine of the angle of elevation of the sun.

So far in this discussion it has been tacitly assumed that there was no cloud in the sky. The effect of cloud is to reduce the average amount of energy reaching the sea surface below it because of the absorption and scattering by the cloud. The effect of cloud may be taken into account by multiplying the mean energy which would arrive in the absence of cloud by a factor $(1-0.07C)$ where $C$ is the proportion in tenths of the sky covered by cloud as seen in plan view. For example if the sky is completely overcast, the value for $C$ would be 10 and the factor would be $(1-0.07 \times 10) = 0.3$, the effect of the cloud then being to reduce the value of $Q_s$ to 0.3 of the clear sky value. For a sky half covered by cloud, $C$ would be 5 and the factor would be 0.65.

In addition to direct sunlight the sea also receives a significant amount of energy from the sky, i.e. sunlight scattered by the atmosphere, clouds, etc. The skylight component increases in importance at high latitudes. For instance, at Stockholm (59°N) for a clear sky in July about 80% of $Q_s$ will be direct sunlight and only 20% skylight. In December, only 13% will be direct sunlight and 87% skylight. It must be remembered however that the total amount of energy reaching the ground will be less in December than in July, and the 87% of skylight in December will represent a smaller energy flow than the 20% in July.

A final factor affecting the incoming short-wave radiation is reflection at the sea surface. This depends on the elevation of the sun and on the state of the sea (calm or waves). It is necessary to calculate the effect separately for direct sunlight which strikes the sea surface at a specific angle of incidence and for skylight which comes from all directions. For a flat sea, the amount of reflection depends on the sun's elevation as in Table 2 below.

TABLE 2

*Reflection coefficient for sea water*

| Sun's elevation: | 90° | 60° | 30° | 20° | 10° | 5° |
|---|---|---|---|---|---|---|
| Amount reflected: | 2 | 3 | 6 | 12 | 35 | 40% |
| Amount transmitted into water: | 98 | 97 | 94 | 88 | 65 | 60% |

For skylight it is calculated that the average amount reflected is about 8%, leaving 92% to enter the water and be absorbed. These figures are all affected somewhat by waves but no very good figures for reflection in their presence are available, and the figures of Table 2 are used as the best available average.

The rate $Q_s$ at which short-wave energy from the sun enters the sea then depends upon all the above factors. Direct measurements of $Q_s$ are made with a pyrheliometer as described in Chapter 6. Average values were published in 1928 by Kimball, in the United States Monthly Weather Review, for each month of the year and for a number of positions on the earth's surface. The considerable increase in numbers of observations in recent years has led to some revision of his values but they are adequate for many purposes. Particularly lacking are adequate observations in the polar regions. The distribution of values of radiant energy arriving at the sea surface, i.e. $Q_s$ not corrected for reflection or cloud, shows interesting variations with position and season. At one extreme we have the equatorial regions where the seasonal variation is small, from a maximum of 690 ly/day to a minimum of 610 ly/day. As one goes north or south from the equator the difference between summer and winter rates increases. At 48°N the range is from 840 to 180 ly/day. At and poleward of the Arctic and Antarctic circles the value decreases substantially to zero in winter, but in the polar summer the maximum daily value is greater than the equatorial maximum. The reason lies in the length of day in the polar summer and the low content of water vapour (an absorber) in the atmosphere.

When the short-wave energy $Q_s$ penetrates into the water it is absorbed and causes the temperature of the water to rise. It is the major source of supply of heat to the oceans. The *absorption* of the energy is progressive as the radiation passes down through the sea and is different for different wavelengths.

TABLE 3

*Percentage of light penetrating to specified depths in sea-water as a percentage of that entering through the surface*

| Depth $z$ (m) | Absorption coefficient, $k$ | | | Clearest ocean water | Turbid coastal water |
|---|---|---|---|---|---|
| | 0·02 | 0·2 | 2 | | |
| 0 | $I_o = 100\%$ | 100% | 100% | 100% | 100% |
| 1 | $I_z =$ 98 | 82 | 14 | 45 | 18 |
| 2 | 96 | 67 | 2 | 39 | 8 |
| 10 | 82 | 14 | 0 | 22 | 0 |
| 50 | 37 | 0 | 0 | 5 | 0 |
| 100 | 14 | 0 | 0 | 0·5 | 0 |

The progressive decrease in energy penetrating downward is expressed by an exponential law, $I_z = I_o \exp(-kz)$, where $I_o$ is the radiation intensity penetrating through the surface, $I_z$ is the remaining intensity at a depth $z$ metres below the surface and $k$ is the absorption coefficient of the water. The effects of depth and of absorption coefficient are shown in Table 3.

The first three columns after the depth column demonstrate the relative influence of the absorption coefficient $k$ and of the depth $z$ on energy of a particular wavelength; the last two columns represent practical conditions in the sea and will be explained below. The column of the table for $k = 0.02$ demonstrates transmission of the most penetrating component, blue-green light, passing through pure water. It only represents an ideal or laboratory situation. Energy penetrates real sea-water less readily than this because of the extra absorption due to suspended particulate matter and to dissolved materials. The absorbing materials are probably chiefly organic acids, the inorganic salts do not show significant absorption at the visible wavelengths. The columns for $k = 0.2$ and 2 are more indicative of the transmission of the most penetrating component through clear ocean water and through very turbid water respectively.

The absorption coefficient $k$ varies considerably with wavelength. For clear ocean water, blue light is absorbed least (penetrates best). At shorter wavelengths (toward the ultra-violet) and at longer wavelengths (in the red and infra-red) the absorption is much greater. The increased absorption in the ultra-violet is not important to the heat budget of the ocean because the amount of energy reaching sea level at such short wavelengths is small. The increased absorption is more important in and beyond the red end of the spectrum where more energy is present in the sun's radiation. Virtually all of the energy shorter than the visible is absorbed in the top metre of water, while the energy of wavelength $1.5\,\mu$ or greater is absorbed in the top one centimetre or less.

In clear ocean water the superior penetration of blue and green light is evident both visually when SCUBA diving and also in colour photographs taken underwater by natural light. Red or yellow objects appear darker in colour or even black as they are viewed at increasing depths because the light of the red end of the spectrum has been absorbed in the upper layers and little is left to be reflected by the object. Blue or green objects retain their colour to greater depths. Materials like kelp which appear brown in the air

3                                                                 D.P.O.

because they reflect blue, green and some yellow or red, appear to turn blue-green as one sees them at increasing depths. Cousteau, in the last chapter of his book *The Silent World*, describes most vividly these visual effects of the selective absorption of sea-water and particularly comments on the brilliant red and orange colours of fish and corals found in deep water to which the red and yellow of sunlight never penetrate.

In more turbid coastal waters all wavelengths are absorbed more than in clear ocean waters but the green-yellow wavelengths penetrate best, while blue and green penetrate less well.

The above remarks have been about the penetration of particular wavelengths. The energy from the sun, $Q_s$, is composed of a range of wavelengths, and as far as the heat budget is concerned the important quantity is the sum total of the energy at all wavelengths penetrating into the water. In any particular body of sea-water the total energy penetration is less than that of the most penetrating component. The last two columns of Table 3 indicate the range of penetrations found in actual sea-water. These are taken from studies by Jerlov during the Swedish Deep Sea Expedition of 1947 to 1948. In the clearest ocean water the figures in Table 3 indicate that in the first metre of depth 55% of the total energy is absorbed and 45% continues beyond 1m, between 1 and 2m a further 6% is absorbed, etc. Also the 5% which penetrates to 50m depth in this water will be in the blue-green part of the spectrum whereas the 8% which penetrates to 2m in the turbid coastal water will be more yellow. In the clear ocean water there is enough light at 50 to 100m to permit a diver to work, but in the more turbid coastal waters all the energy may have been absorbed by 10m depth.

In addition to its significance for the heat budget, the penetration of radiation into the sea is of interest to biologists in connection with the photosynthetic activity of phytoplankton and algae and with the behaviour of zooplankton and fish. Some of the methods available for measuring the absorption or transmission of radiation through the sea are described in Chapter 6.

The *back radiation* term, $Q_b$, in the heat budget takes account of the net amount of energy lost by the sea as long-wave radiation. The value of the term $Q_b$ is actually the difference between the energy radiated outward from the sea surface in proportion to the fourth power of its absolute temperature, and that received by the sea from the atmosphere which also radiates at a rate proportional to the fourth power of its absolute temperature. The outward radiation from the sea is always greater than the inward radiation from the atmosphere and so $Q_b$ always represents a loss of heat energy from the sea.

The long-wave back radiation $Q_b$ is determined by calculating the rate of loss of long-wave energy outward from the sea from Stefan's Law and subtracting from this the long-wave radiation coming in from the atmosphere. This is measured with a radiometer as described in Chapter 6.

If direct measurements of $Q_b$ are not available it is possible to calculate the heat loss by means of data published by Ångström. He showed that the net rate of loss depends upon the absolute temperature of the sea surface itself and upon the water-vapour content of the atmosphere immediately above the sea. The temperature of the sea determines the rate of outward flow of energy. The water-vapour content effectively determines the inward flow from the atmosphere because the water-vapour in the atmosphere is the main source of its long-wave radiation. Ångström's data were published in the form of a table of values of $Q_b$ as a function of water temperature and of water-vapour pressure in millimetres of mercury. The latter quantity is not measured directly as a rule but instead it is determined from the air temperature and the relative humidity. The latter is easily measured by means of a psychrometer (wet and dry bulb thermometers). Sverdrup adapted Ångström's data to enable $Q_b$ to be read off a graph which is entered with the sea surface temperature and the relative humidity. In preparing this graph it was assumed that the air temperature just above the sea surface was substantially the same as the sea surface temperature, as is generally the case. Over the range of sea temperature from $-2°$ to $30°C$ and from 70 to 100% relative humidity, the values of $Q_b$ range from 280 to 225 ly/day. The higher rates occur at low temperatures and low humidity and vice versa.

The value of $Q_b$ decreases as the sea surface temperature increases for the following reason. A rise of sea surface temperature causes an increase in the outward radiation from the sea but at the same time is accompanied by an increase in humidity in the atmosphere immediately above it. The temperature of this lower atmosphere follows that of the sea. The amount of water-vapour however increases exponentially, i.e. more rapidly than the temperature, with the result that the atmosphere's radiation down into the sea increases more rapidly than the sea's outward radiation. The net result is a decrease in $Q_b$ (i.e. a reduced loss from the sea) as the sea temperature increases. If only the atmospheric humidity increases, the inward radiation from atmosphere to sea increases and therefore the net $Q_b$ decreases.

The back radiation term does not change much either daily or seasonally because neither the sea temperature nor the relative humidity over the sea change much in these intervals. For instance, a seasonal change of sea temperature from 10° to 20°C would give rise to a change in outward radiation proportional to $293^4/283^4$ or about 1·14, i.e. only a 14% increase. At the same time the atmospheric radiation inward would increase and reduce the net rate of loss below this figure. The small seasonal and geographic change of $Q_b$ is in contrast to the large changes in $Q_s$.

The above values for $Q_b$ are all for the clear sky condition. In the presence of cloud the incoming radiation is increased so that the net rate of loss, $Q_b$, decreases. The effect of cloud may be allowed for by multiplying the clear sky values for $Q_b$ by the factor $(1-0.08C)$ where $C$ is the amount in tenths of sky covered by substantial cloud (i.e. cirrus cloud is less effective than thicker cloud like cumulus). From this it is seen that with the sky completely covered with cloud ($C = 10$) the value of the factor is 0·2, i.e. the loss of energy by long-wave radiation is sharply reduced by cloud. This effect of cloud is well known on land where the frost which results from radiation cooling (i.e. the $Q_b$ term for land) is more frequent on clear nights than on cloudy ones. The reason for the big difference between clear and cloudy conditions is that the atmosphere, particularly its water-vapour content, is relatively transparent to radiation in the range from about 8 to 13 $\mu$ which includes the peak of the radiation spectrum for a body of the temperature of the sea. In clear weather, energy between 8 and 13 $\mu$ wavelength radiated by the sea (and the land) passes through the wavelength "window" in the atmosphere and on out into space where it is lost from the earth system. Liquid water, however, is not transparent in this wavelength range and the water drops in cloud absorb the long-wave energy radiated from earth and radiate some of it back.

It should be noted here that for energy in this long-wave part of the spectrum, water has a very high absorption coefficient. The incoming long-wave radiation from the atmosphere is all absorbed, not in the top metres of the sea, but in the top millimetre. Similarly the outward radiation is determined by the temperature of the literal surface or skin of the sea. In practice the "sea surface" temperature which is measured is that of a bucket of water dipped from the upper half metre or so. If the sea surface is disturbed by wind and waves the bucket temperature is assumed to be reasonably representative of the skin temperature but very little work has been done in this skin layer. It may seem rather trivial at first sight to go out to study the top millimetre of the sea, but apart from the heat budget aspect it is probable that other processes such as the early stages of wind generated waves are determined by stresses in this surface skin.

When the sea surface becomes covered with a layer of ice, and especially if snow covers the ice, there is a marked change in the heat radiation budget. For a water surface, the average proportion of short-wave radiation (sun + sky) reflected is relatively small (10 to 15%) and the proportion absorbed therefore large. For ice or snow, the proportion of short-wave radiation reflected is much larger (50 to 80%) leaving a smaller proportion to be absorbed. However, the size of the $Q_b$ loss term is much the same for ice as for water, and the result is a smaller net gain ($Q_s - Q_b$) by ice and snow surfaces than by water. In consequence, once ice forms it tends to be maintained. It has been estimated that the balance in the Arctic Sea is relatively fine and that if the sea-ice were once melted the increased net heat gain $(Q_s - Q_b)$ might maintain the Arctic Sea free of ice. This, however, would increase the amount of evaporation and there might be marked increases in precipitation on the high north latitude lands which at present receive a relatively small precipitation (mostly as snow in the winter). It should be emphasized that this latter idea about possible changes in the Arctic is very speculative as it is difficult to be sure that the factors that might be changed have been correctly assessed, or indeed that all the factors that would affect the situation have been included. However, it is often by making predictions and then observing their success or otherwise that we test our understanding of natural processes.

When we start to consider the *conduction term* $Q_h$ a new aspect of oceanography comes into the picture. The reason that heat may be gained or lost from the sea surface is that there is often a temperature gradient in the air above the sea. If the temperature in the air decreases upward away from the surface of the sea, heat will be conducted away from the sea and $Q_h$ will be a loss term. If the temperature decreases downward toward the sea surface, heat will be conducted down into it and $Q_h$ will be a gain term. In principle the rate of loss or gain of heat is equal to the temperature gradient in the air multiplied by a coefficient of heat conductivity $K$, i.e. $Q_h = -K \cdot dT/dz$. In small volumes, where the air as a whole is stationary, the process of heat conduction is due only to the random thermal motions of the air molecules (provided that convection is avoided). The coefficient $K$ is then referred to as that for "molecular" conductivity of heat. This quantity is a constant for a particular gas at a particular temperature. However, in nature, and in particular over the sea surface, the air is usually in motion (wind) and the motion is turbulent. A consequence of this is that the air eddies, which consist of bulk movements of the air, carry air properties with them. These properties then tend to move down the property gradient, e.g. heat from higher to lower temperature, but at a much greater rate than is the case when movements of molecules only are concerned. It is possible to define a quantity called the "eddy" conductivity for heat $(A_h)$ where there is turbulent motion, and to describe the rate of heat transfer by the product of this and the temperature gradient, i.e. $Q_h = -A_h \cdot dT/dz$. It is the introduction of this concept of eddy transfer which is the new idea referred to at the start of this paragraph. It has been introduced here to apply to the conduction of heat through the air above the sea. It applies equally to the transfer or diffusion of water-vapour through the air as will be described in the section on $Q_e$. It also applies to the conduction of heat and the diffusion of salt through the sea where the motion is usually turbulent. Under turbulent conditions the eddy transfer rate for a property is generally so much larger than the molecular rate that the latter can be neglected.

The reason why the introduction of eddy conduction introduces some difficulty is that the eddy conductivity $A_h$ is not a constant quantity, even at constant temperature, as is the molecular conductivity $K$. The eddy conductivity depends on the character of the turbulence in the air. This, in turn, depends on various factors such as the wind speed and the size of the ripples or waves on the sea surface. We do not yet know enough about turbulence in nature to be able to say with any certainty what the value of the eddy coefficient will be in every situation. All that we can really say is that if we happen to have measured the eddy conductivity on a previous occasion when the wind conditions, etc. were much the same, then the eddy conductivity will probably be much the same. Since the determining factor is the character of the turbulence which is impossible to judge by eye and difficult to measure, even with sophisticated instruments, this leaves us in an unhappy situation. It would not be so bad if the eddy conductivity only varied a small amount with wind conditions; unfortunately it may vary over a range of ten or a hundred fold. This whole problem of eddy transfer of properties in fluids is a part of the more general problem of turbulence which is one of the most pressing problems in physics requiring solution at the present time. Research on various aspects is under way and we are gradually acquiring some understanding of this aspect of fluid mechanics.

However, if we are to study the heat budget we need some value for the heat conduction term $Q_h$. It will be shown that it can be related to the evaporation term $Q_e$ and we will therefore put aside the question of determining $Q_h$ for the moment until after we have discussed evaporation.

Before going on to this, some points about $Q_h$ will be mentioned. In situations where the sea is warmer than the air above it, there will be a loss of heat from the sea because of the direction of the temperature gradient.  However, the phenomenon of convection will also occur and assist the transfer of heat away from the sea surface. Convection occurs because the air near to the warm sea gets heated, expands, and rises carrying heat away rapidly. In the opposite case where the sea is cooler than the air, the latter is cooled where it is in contact with the sea, becomes denser, and therefore tends to stay where it is and the phenomenon of convection does not come into play.  The consequence is that for the same number of degrees difference in temperature between sea and air, the rate of loss of heat when the sea is the warmer is greater than the rate of gain of heat when the sea is the cooler. In the tropics the sea is generally warmer than the air, on the average by about $0 \cdot 8 \mathrm{C}°$, and the result is that $Q_h$ is a loss term. In middle and high latitudes the temperature difference is more variable but on the whole the sea is warmer than the air and consequently here also $Q_h$ is generally a loss term.

Finally, the *evaporation term* $Q_e$ is an important term but is not easy to determine. Basically there are three methods used to determine $Q_e$. Two depend on measurements of the rate of evaporation of water while the third is a difference method.

The reason why evaporation enters into the heat budget is that for evaporation to occur it is necessary either to supply heat from an outside source or for the heat to be taken from the remaining liquid. The second is the more usual case for the sea. (It is the reason why one often feels cold when one stands with one's wet body exposed to the wind after swimming.) Therefore evaporation, besides implying loss of volume of water, also implies loss of heat. The rate of heat loss is $Q_e = F_e . L_t$, where $F_e$ is the rate of evaporation of water in grams per minute per square centimetre of sea surface, and $L_t$ is the latent heat of evaporation. For pure water this depends on temperature as $L_t = 596 - 0.52T$ cal/g where the temperature $T$ of the water is measured in degrees Celsius. At 10°C, the latent heat is about 591 cal/g, much greater than the more familiar value of about 540 cal/g at the boiling point. The first two methods for determining $Q_e$ then depend on measuring $F_e$.

The most obvious way to do this would appear to be to set out a pan of sea-water on deck and measure its rate of evaporation by weighing it at intervals. A better way to determine the water loss is to determine the salinity of the water at intervals and calculate the loss of water from the increase in salinity. There are, however, some difficulties because the surface of the water in the pan is not in the same situation as the sea surface. The pan can be suspended so that the water does not slop over the edge as the ship moves but it is necessary to see that no spray gets into it. This necessitates using screens but these at once change the wind flow over the pan and therefore the rate of evaporation. The water in a pan is likely to warm up to a higher temperature than that in the sea itself and this will increase the evaporation rate. A more serious difficulty is that the pan has to be at about deck level which is likely to be several metres above sea level. The water-vapour pressure at this height may be appreciably less than that at the sea surface and therefore the rate of evaporation from the pan will be greater than the true rate from the sea. Even on land, in studies of evaporation from reservoirs, it is difficult to get consistent results with pans of different designs. From the few careful studies which have been made at sea it appears that the evaporation from a pan at deck level is likely to average about twice the true rate from the sea surface. The most detailed measurements and studies have been made by Wüst who found that the average amount of evaporation per year over the world ocean is 93 cm, i.e. equivalent to the sea surface sinking by 93cm due to evaporation. The local values of evaporation vary from minima of about 8cm/year in high latitudes rising to maxima of up to 146 cm/year in the tropics north and south of the equator, and decreasing to about 110cm/year at the equator. The high values in the tropics are associated with the north and south trade winds and the lower values at the equator with the less strong and less steady winds of the doldrums. The high values of evaporation in the trade wind regions are the reason for the high surface salinity values there (Figs. 3 and 11).

The pan method being inconvenient and uncertain, it is usual to use other means for determining the evaporation. In principle, $F_e$ could be measured by the application of a formula of the type: $F_e = -A_e . df/dz$, where $A_e$ is the eddy diffusion coefficient for water-vapour through the atmosphere and $df/dz$ is the gradient of water-vapour concentration (humidity) in the air above the sea surface. Unfortunately we are up against the same difficulty for water-vapour diffusion as for heat conduction, because the eddy diffusivity $A_e$ also has a wide range of values depending on the turbulence in the air. In practice a semi-empirical flow formula is frequently used in the form: $F_e = 0.014(e_s - e_a) . W$ grams per day per square centimetre of sea surface. In this formula $e_s$ is the saturated vapour pressure over the sea-water and $e_a$ is the actual vapour pressure in the air at a height of 10m above sea level, both of these pressures being expressed in millibars (1013mb = 760mm of mercury). The saturated vapour pressure over sea-water $(e_s)$ is a little less than that over distilled water $(e_d)$. For a salinity of 35‰, $e_s = 0.98e_d$ at the same temperature. The saturated vapour pressure over distilled water may be obtained from tables of physical or meteorological constants. If the water-vapour content in the air is given as relative humidity then the value $e_a$ is equal to the saturated vapour pressure over distilled water at the temperature of the air multiplied by the relative humidity expressed as a fraction, not as a percentage. For example, at an air temperature of 15°C the saturated vapour pressure is 12·8mm Hg. If the relative humidity is 85% then the actual vapour pressure in the air is $12·8 \times 0·85 =$

10·9 mm Hg.=14·5 mb. In the formula above, $W$ is the wind speed in metres per second at 10 m above sea level.

This practical formula is basically a simplified version of the theoretical eddy diffusion formula above. In the theoretical formula $df/dz$ is the vertical humidity gradient, $df$ being the change in humidity over a vertical distance $dz$. In the practical formula $(e_s-e_a)$ is the change in humidity over the vertical distance $dz$ of 10 m between the sea surface and the height where $e_a$ is measured. (In the practical formula the 10 does not appear explicitly, having been absorbed in the numerical constant.) The $W$ of the practical formula represents the variation of $A_e$ in an elementary fashion. The values of $A_e$ do not necessarily vary directly with the wind speed but we expect turbulence to increase in some way as wind speed increases and therefore eddy diffusion should increase as the wind speed increases. Hence the use of $W$ in the formula does at least give some variation of eddy diffusion in what is certainly the right direction. The actual numerical value of $A_e$ is, of course, not the same as the wind speed; again the factor of proportionality between them is hidden in the numerical constant in the practical formula.

In most regions of the ocean, it turns out that $e_s$ is greater than $e_a$ and therefore as all the other terms in the practical formula are positive, the value of $F_e$ is positive and so is $Q_e$. As this is entered in the heat budget equation as $(-Q_e)$ it represents a loss of heat from the sea due to evaporation in most cases. In fact, as long as the sea temperature is more than about 0·3C° greater than the air temperature, there will be a loss of heat from the sea due to evaporation. Only in a few regions is the reverse the case, when the air temperature is greater than the sea temperature and the humidity is sufficient to cause condensation of water-vapour from the air into the sea. This results in a loss of heat from the air into the sea. The Grand Banks off Newfoundland, and the coastal seas off Northern California in summer are examples of regions where the heat flow is into the sea. The fogs that occur in these regions are a result of the cooling of the atmosphere.

The third method for estimating $Q_e$ is the heat budget method. If, in the full heat budget equation as stated at the beginning of this section, we consider the situation when $Q_v = 0$ (no advection) and when $Q_T = 0$ (steady state), and we introduce the quantity $R = Q_h/Q_e$ called *Bowen's Ratio*, then $Q_e = (Q_s - Q_b)/(1+R)$. From this equation, if we can obtain values of $Q_s$ and $Q_b$ and can determine $R$, we can obtain a value for $Q_e$. The two radiation terms have already been discussed and it remains to discuss $R$. This is the ratio of the heat conduction term to the evaporation term. Earlier it was explained that the molecular transfer rates for heat and for water-vapour are considered negligible by comparison with the eddy transfer rates associated with turbulence. The expressions for $Q_h = -A_h \cdot \mathrm{d}T/\mathrm{d}z$ and $Q_e = -A_e \cdot \mathrm{d}f/\mathrm{d}z$ are similar because the transfer mechanism due to turbulent eddy movements of the air above the sea is of the same physical nature for both. If one goes further and assumes that the numerical values of $A_h$ and $A_e$ are the same, then these two terms will cancel out in Bowen's Ratio, leaving only the ratios of the temperatures and the humidity gradients. Each of these gradients may be expressed approximately by the difference of the respective quantity (temperature or humidity) between the sea surface and a level above the sea surface. If the temperature and humidity gradients are both measured over the same range of height $\mathrm{d}z$ between the sea surface and some height above sea level (e.g. on the ship's mast or bridge), then the $\mathrm{d}z$'s will also cancel in Bowen's Ratio. This then reduces to the simple form: $R = 0.64 (T_s - T_a)/(e_s - e_a)$. Here $T_s$ and $T_a$ represent the temperature at sea level and at 10 metres height respectively, while $e_s$ and $e_a$ represent water-vapour pressures in millibars at the same positions. Both temperature and water-vapour pressure may be measured relatively easily. Hence a value for $R$ is obtained, and this may be used in the earlier equation together with measurements of $Q_s$ and $Q_b$ to obtain a value for $Q_e$.

Before going on it should be pointed out that the above simplified practical formula for determining $R$ from the meteorological observations depends on the assumption that $A_h$ and $A_e$ are numerically the same. This is based on the simple argument that the transfers of heat and water-vapour are both due to the turbulent motion of the air above the sea. The process of turbulence consists in the transfer of properties from larger to successively smaller eddies and eventually, at the end of the scale, molecular transfer must play a part. While the eddy transfer coefficients for heat, water-vapour and other properties tend to have much the same value for high turbulence, they are not numerically equal for low turbulence. The assumption that they are equal when simplifying the Bowen's Ratio formula is therefore an approximation but it seems to be a reasonably good one, judged on the basis of consistency of deductions obtained by its use compared with other evidence.

Average values for $R$ based on many sets of meteorological data are of the order of $+0 \cdot 1$ in equatorial and tropical regions and increase to about $+0 \cdot 45$ at $70°N$. Remembering that $R = Q_h/Q_e$ this indicates that the heat flow term is usually smaller than the evaporation term. It should be noted that the average values for $R$ are positive because $T_s$ and $e_s$ are usually greater than $T_a$ and $e_a$ respectively. Therefore both of the difference terms in the expression for $R$ are positive. However, it is possible for $R$ to be negative in the regions where the sea temperature $T_s$ is less than the air temperature $T_a$. A negative value for $R$ indicates the unusual condition of $Q_h$ representing heat flow into the sea.

If a value for $R$ were available, then $Q_e$ could be obtained from the relation $Q_e = (Q_s - Q_b)/(1 + R)$ derived above. This relation however depends on the two assumptions that $Q_T$ and $Q_v$ are both zero, and it is of limited application. It is not too difficult to check on the first assumption but the second requires detailed current measurements and these are among the most time and effort consuming aspects of experimental physical oceanography if they are to be done well. The heat budget method for determining $Q_e$ is most useful for large areas for checking heat budget estimates obtained by other methods. In practice, $Q_e$ is usually obtained from the semi-empirical flow formula, and then with a value for $R$ we can calculate $Q_h = R \cdot Q_e$.

The value for the rate of loss of heat by evaporation from the ocean averages 170 ly/day, but ranges up to over 300 ly/day at mid-latitudes in the western North Pacific and 400 ly/day in the western North Atlantic. The basic reason for the high values being found in the west is that they are associated with the circulation of the oceans. The westward flowing equatorial currents turn north along the western boundary of the northern oceans and carry warm water, with a relatively high vapour pressure, to higher latitudes where the air temperatures and vapour pressure are lower. This gives rise to a high humidity-gradient resulting in a high upward flow of water-vapour from the sea. The maximum values for $Q_e$ occur at the western side of the ocean, and they occur in the winter. The latter fact appears surprising at first, but is simply because the water temperature, and therefore the associated vapour pressure of the northward flowing water does not decrease much in winter, but the air temperature does decrease and with it the water-vapour pressure in the air. In other words, the term $(e_s - e_a)$ is greater in winter than in summer in the western parts of the oceans and consequently the heat loss by evaporation is greater in winter.

The loss by heat conduction $(Q_h)$ averages 20 to 40 ly/day and is much less than that due to evaporation. It also shows maximum values at the western sides of the oceans and in winter.

The above statements have emphasized the northern oceans because there are more data available for them than for the southern oceans, but generally speaking the changes are believed to be substantially the same as one goes poleward from the equator in both hemispheres.

In Fig. 13a are shown the annual average values for the heat budget terms in the northern hemisphere. Some of the features which are shown by this figure are that the direct sun's radiation (corrected for cloud) is most important to about 50°N but that beyond this the skylight component is equally important, and that while the evaporation loss term decreases markedly toward the pole, the back radiation term is much the same at all latitudes. The balance between the gain and loss terms (Fig. 13b) shows a net gain of energy from the equator to 30° N and a net loss beyond this. At first sight there appears to be a much greater loss than gain but this is not really the case. The quantities shown in Fig. 13a are in ly/day, i.e. they are the rate of heat flow per square centimetre

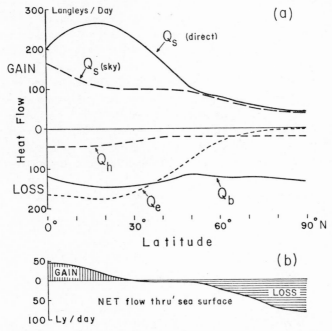

FIG. 13. *Values of the heat flow terms through the sea surface as a function of latitude.*

of sea surface. To obtain the total flow in or out for any latitude zone one must multiply by the total sea area in that zone. This area is less at high than low latitudes and with this correction the gain and loss are more nearly, but not exactly, balanced. As there is no indication that the oceans as a whole are getting warmer or colder we would expect an exact balance. We must conclude that the fault lies in our having insufficiently accurate knowledge of the individual heat flow terms to permit the budget to be balanced exactly.

For the earth as a whole (land and sea), and averaged over the year, $Q_s$ is greater than $Q_b$ between the equator and about 40°N, and there is a net gain of heat by radiation at these lower latitudes. At higher latitudes, $Q_s$ is less than $Q_b$ and therefore there is a net loss of heat by radiation. Since the average temperatures over the earth remain substantially constant we conclude that there must be a net advective flow of heat to the north, from the lower latitudes of net radiation gain to the higher ones of net loss. This heat flow toward the pole is effected both by the atmosphere and by the ocean. These transport warm air or water toward the pole and cooler air or water toward the equator. In the northern hemisphere the contribution to the heat transport by the ocean rises to a maximum at 30°N and then decreases. The atmosphere's contribution increases to about 40°N and then decreases. From the equator to 10°N the ocean and atmosphere contribute equally to the northward advection of heat; beyond this the atmosphere is the main agent.

CHAPTER SIX

# Instruments and Methods

BEFORE describing the techniques and methods of physical ocean-ography something must be said about the aims and limitations of field observations.

The fundamental goal of the physical oceanographer has been stated as to determine the circulation of the oceans. The obvious way would seem to be to go out to sea with current meters and to measure it directly. Unfortunately, most current meters only give information on the velocity of the water within a few metres of the instrument itself, and very little experience indicates that large variations in current velocity can occur even over small distances as well as over small time intervals. Also it is only possible in the present state of current meter development for one ship to measure currents at few points at any one time, and the number of oceanographic ships and of oceanographers to man them is limited. In consequence, direct measurements of currents have to be restricted to key localities of limited area and for purposes such as testing specific theories. The total of direct measurements of subsurface currents has provided only a small portion of our observed knowledge of the ocean circulation.

Failing a sufficiency of direct measurements, the synoptic ocean-ographer has been forced to use indirect ones. The calculation of currents by the geostrophic method is one of these but this is regarded as being in the field of dynamical oceanography and will not be considered here. The chief indirect method has been to observe the distributions of water properties, which can be done more expeditiously than observing currents, and to deduce the currents from these distributions. In the majority of cases, this method only reveals the path followed by the water and gives little information on speed. The path is better than nothing but the synoptic oceanographer is always on the look out for any characteristic of the property distributions which will give him an idea of speed as well as direction. The rate of oxygen consumption has been used in a tentative manner but the built-in clock of radioactive decay offers more promise as it is independent of the physical character of the ocean environment. Carbon-14 ($C^{14}$) and deuterium, for example have been used but in the sea their use as clocks is by no means straightforward.

Even when using the water property distributions the time factor enters. The ships available for oceanographic research on the high seas (e.g. Pl. 1) have speeds of only 10 to 15 knots, the distances to be covered are large, and the time taken at each station to sample the water at a sufficient number of depths is measured in hours. The *Meteor* spent two years in one study of the South Atlantic alone, and for even a small area it may take weeks or months to complete a survey. It is therefore impracticable to obtain a truly simultaneous picture of the ocean, and the synoptic oceanographer has to make the assumption that when he analyses them the data from his cruise or cruises may be considered as simultaneous. It is certainly fortunate that such checks as are available suggest that the main features of the open ocean are in a reasonably steady state and therefore the oceanographer's assumption is usually justified. In fact, it is when he comes into shallow coastal waters that difficulties arise because the variations in properties with position are often greater and the period of change shorter than in the deep sea.


## INSTRUMENTS

In the following pages some of the basic instruments used in physical oceanography will be described, emphasizing the principles rather than attempting to give detailed descriptions.

*Winches, Wire, etc.*

One of the most essential pieces of equipment on an oceanographic vessel is a winch with a drum holding wire cable on which instruments are lowered into the sea. For lowering bathythermographs and small instruments, a light duty winch with some 500m of 2 to 3mm diameter steel wire and a motor of 1 to 3 h.p. is used For water sampling and temperature measurement, a medium duty winch (Pl. 2) with 2000 to 5000m of 4mm diameter wire and a 10 to 20 h.p. motor may be used, while for heavier work, such as dredging, coring etc., winches with up to 15,000m of 10 to 20mm wire and 100 to 200 h.p. have been used. The wire used is multi-strand wire cable for flexibility, and made of galvanized or stainless steel (more expensive) to resist corrosion. (Sea-water is one of the most corrosive substances known, given time to act.) The winches must be capable of reeling the wire in or out at speeds up to 100m/min but must also be controllable in speed so that an instrument can be brought accurately to a position for operation or to where it can be reached for recovery.

*Depth Measurement*

The determination of the depth to which an instrument has been lowered is not always easy. The wire is passed over a "meter wheel" (Pl. 5) which is simply a pulley of known circumference with a counter attached to the pulley to count the number of turns, thus giving a direct indication of the length of wire passed out over it. This length gives a maximum value for the depth which the instrument on the wire has reached. In calm conditions with negligible currents this will be the actual depth. More often the ship is drifting because of the wind or surface currents and the wire is then neither straight nor vertical so that the actual depth will be less, sometimes much less, than the length of wire paid out.

The depth of an instrument can be determined by measuring

the hydrostatic pressure at its level, as this is proportional to depth. One pressure measuring device is a bourdon tube moving the slider of an electrical potentiometer, but this needs an electrical cable to transmit the depth information to the ship. It may be accurate to $\pm 0.5$ to $1\%$. The 'Vibratron' pressure gauge applies the water pressure to vary the tension in a stretched wire which is caused to vibrate electromagnetically. The frequency of vibration depends on the wire tension and hence on the depth. The vibration frequency is determined to give a measurement of depth to about $\pm 0.25\%$ accuracy. The use of the protected/unprotected thermometer combination for the determination of depth is described in the section on temperature measurement.

## Current Measurement

There are two basic ways to describe fluid flow, the Eulerian method in which the velocity (i.e. speed and direction) is stated at every point in the fluid, and the Lagrangian method in which the path followed by each fluid particle is stated as a function of time. In both cases the statements are usually made with respect to axes which are stationary relative to the solid earth. In theoretical studies the Eulerian method is usually the easier to use, but in describing the circulation of the oceans, as in Chapter 7, the Lagrangian method is used most often.

The simplest *Eulerian current meter* is the Chesapeake Bay Institute "drag". This consists simply of two crossed rectangles of wood (Fig. 14a), weighted and suspended by a thin wire. When the drag is immersed, the frictional force of the current pulls the wire to an angle from the vertical. The current speed is related by a simple formula to the size of the drag, its weight in water, and the angle of the wire from the vertical. This angle is measured to determine the current. The device is simple, cheap to make and quick to use from an anchored ship. It is limited to depths of a few tens of metres because the current drag on the wire increases with length and complicates the interpretation of the wire angle at greater lengths.

Perhaps the most used Eulerian instrument is the Ekman current meter (Pl. 3). This consists of a multi-blade propellor, about 10 cm in diameter, which is mounted on low friction bearings in a framework which is attached to the end of a wire and lowered to the depth to be investigated. The propeller is held stationary by a catch until

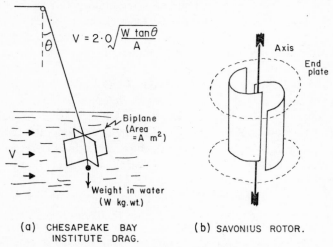

(a) CHESAPEAKE BAY
INSTITUTE DRAG.

(b) SAVONIUS ROTOR.

FIG. 14. (a) *Principle of use of the Chesapeake Bay Institute drag for current measurement*, (b) *simple form of Savonius rotor for current meters.*

released by the impact of a metal weight ("messenger", Pl. 6) which is slid down the wire. After being allowed to rotate for a measured time the propellor is stopped by a second messenger, and then the meter is brought back on deck and the number of revolutions read from a set of pointers geared to the propellor. The water speed is directly proportional to the number of revolutions per minute from about 2 to 250 cm/sec. The direction of the current is recorded in a most ingenious manner. The whole instrument is free to rotate on the end of the wire, and a fin at the rear causes it to point into the current. At intervals, while the propellor is turning, small bronze balls are released to fall on to the top of a magnetic compass needle, run down a trough on its upper side, and fall thence into a tray divided into 10° sectors. As the compass and trough remain fixed in the magnetic meridian while the remainder of the instrument, including the tray, is oriented by the current, the particular sector into which the balls drop gives an indication of the current direction. The whole arrangement sounds rather far-fetched but this instrument does work at sea, a strong recommendation for oceanographic equipment. It has the disadvantage of being discontinuous and having to be retrieved for each measurement.

It should be mentioned here that one of the fundamental difficulties in Eulerian current measurement is determining the direction component of the velocity. When the current meter is out of sight below the surface the only frame of reference available to it is the earth's magnetic field. This yields only a small torque to turn a direction indicator and herein lies one of the instrument designer's difficulties.

The Roberts' current meter also uses a propellor for speed measurement but instead of recording on the instrument itself the information is transmitted electrically to the surface. The propellor carries a small magnet which, as it rotates, drags round a second magnet in a water tight container. This second magnet drives a counting mechanism which transmits its information to the surface through an electrical cable. The current direction from a compass is also transmitted to the surface. The original type of Roberts' meter is suspended from an anchored buoy containing a radio transmitter which retransmits the current information to a mother ship which can collect information from several such buoys simultaneously. The Roberts' meter is also available for use directly from a ship and has been used in this way for deep-sea observations as will be described later.

One disadvantage of the propellor type current meter is that up-and-down motion, as when the ship rolls, may cause the propellor to turn and cause inaccuracies in the speed measurement. A hollow cylinder with its axis horizontal mounted round the propellor minimizes this effect. An alternative to the propellor is the Savonius rotor which is not sensitive to vertical motion. It consists of two half hollow cylinders mounted on a vertical axis with flat end-plates (Fig. 14b, Pl. 4) and has the advantage of producing a large torque even in small currents. The rotor is made of plastic to be neutrally buoyant to reduce bearing friction so that it is sensitive to currents of as little as 0·1 cm/sec. The rotor actuates an electrical transmitter to send a series of pulses (many per second) to the ship where a pulse frequency measuring instrument indicates or records the current speed (Pl. 4).

A different method for current measurement is to use the rate of cooling of an electrically heated wire as a measure of the fluid speed past it. This is the hot wire anemometer. A thin wire or film of metal about a millimetre long is exposed to the fluid flow and maintained at constant temperature by automatically adjusting the electric current through it so that the Joule heating is exactly equal to the rate of loss to the fluid. The magnitude of the electric current is then a measure of the water speed. This device has the advantages of small size and very rapid response to flow variations which make it particularly suitable for the measurement of turbulent fluctuations of flow speeds.

Another fundamentally different principle, which was originally suggested by Faraday, is to use the EMF induced in a conductor moving in a magnetic field. Sea-water is a conductor and when it flows across the lines of force of the earth's magnetic field an EMF, $E = B.L.v$, will be generated where $v$ is the water speed, $L$ the width of the current and $B$ the strength of the component of the earth's magnetic field in a direction perpendicular to the direction of both $v$ and $L$. For a horizontal current along a channel, $B$ would be the vertical component of the earth's field. Some of the earliest measurements by this "electromagnetic method" were of the tidal currents through the English Channel, and long series of measurements of the Florida Current have been made between Florida and

Cuba. The basic equipment required is a recording millivoltmeter and two electrodes to dip into the sea. The electrodes are best placed one on each side of the current and so a further requirement is an insulated connecting wire to the farther electrode. Unused commercial cable circuits have often been used for this purpose. One source of error is the finite electrical conductivity of the sea bottom which allows an electrical current to flow due to the induced EMF and so reduces the value of the EMF observed between the electrodes across the current. This introduces a constant scaling-factor which may be determined by making some current measure-ments with another type of meter while the electromagnetic system is in operation.

An adaptation of this arrangement, developed by von Arx, is the geomagnetic electrokinetograph (GEK) which is used from a ship at sea. In this, the two electrodes which are 30 to 100 m apart are towed in line behind the ship and connected to a recording milli-voltmeter. If an ocean current is carrying the ship and the electrodes in a direction perpendicular to the wire joining the latter there will be an EMF induced in the wire. This EMF is ideally proportional to the wire length, the earth's magnetic field and the speed of the current perpendicular to the wire. Therefore measurement of the EMF will yield the current if the other factors are known and remain constant. The GEK works best for surface currents over relatively stationary deep water, so that the latter can short circuit the EMF generated simultaneously in the surface water and leave the EMF in the wire uncompensated and measurable. In shallow water the short circuiting effect of the subsurface water may be incomplete and the observed EMF will be less than the theoretical one by an uncertain amount. As the GEK only yields the component of current perpendicular to the wire, it is necessary to change the ship's course for a few minutes at intervals in order to measure a second component to permit adding the two vectorially to determine the total current velocity.

One requirement for either electromagnetic method is stable electrodes so that varying electrochemical EMFs will not complicate the measurement. Silver wire with silver chloride deposited on it is the most satisfactory electrode for use in the sea.

The simplest *Lagrangian current indicator* is an object floating in the water with a minimum surface exposed to catch the wind. The so-called "drift pole", a wooden pole a few metres long and weighted to float with only $\frac{1}{2}$ to 1m emergent, is often used to determine surface currents close to landmarks. Such a pole is simply allowed to drift, and its position is determined at intervals either from the shore or by approaching it in a small boat and fixing its position relative to the shore. Sheets of paper or patches of dye, such as sodium fluorescein, which can be photographed at intervals from a high point of land or from an aircraft are also used.

To determine the path followed by a pollutant, such as sewage or an industrial waste, it is often possible to use the substance itself as a tracer. Samples of water are collected from a grid of positions near the source and in likely directions of flow, and the pollutant concentration determined by chemical analysis. Radioactive materials seem attractive as tracers of water movement, and they were successfully used after some of the early Pacific atom-bomb tests. However, in the quantities needed in the sea the cost is often prohibitive, and there is always some reluctance expressed by non-oceanographers to the release of radioactive materials in the neigh-bourhood of communities or commercial fisheries. A very convenient artificial tracer is the red dye rhodamine-B. This can be detected at extremely small concentrations (less than 1 part in $10^{10}$ of water) by its fluorescence, using relatively simple instruments, and it is also non-toxic at such dilutions. It is only practical to use it in coastal waters, as the quantities required to "tag" open ocean water masses would be impractically large.

A sophisticated drift pole was introduced in 1955 for the measurement of subsurface currents. This is the neutral-buoyancy float invented by Swallow of the National Institute of Oceanography in England. This "Swallow float" makes use of the fact that the density in the sea increases with depth. The float can be adjusted before use so that it will sink to a selected density level, i.e. depth, when released in the water. It then remains at this depth and drifts with the water around it. The float contains equipment to send out sound pulses at intervals and it can be followed by listening to it through hydrophones from the ship. The ship chases the float and at the same time continuously determines its own position. It thereby determines the direction and speed of drift of the float and the water mass in which it is located. A limitation with this instrument is that one ship can follow only a very small number of floats at one time. If several floats are released, e.g. at different levels, it is quite likely that they will be perverse and drift off in different directions and the ship may not be able to keep track of them all. The Swallow float is really the first oceanographic instrument to give us reliable information on the direction and speed of deep currents, and as is usual when one ventures into a new area some of the results obtained have been unexpected (e.g. deep currents in the Atlantic, Chapter 7).

In Chapter 7 a description is given of the Cromwell Current in the Pacific Equatorial Current system, and it is appropriate to say something about the techniques of measurement which yielded the new quantitative data. The measurement of currents in the open ocean, particularly subsurface currents, has always been considered to be one of the most difficult tasks facing the physical oceanographer in the field. It is for this reason that he has had to rely on current directions deduced from water property distributions for much of his knowledge of subsurface ocean currents. The fundamental difficulty is that the currents are generally small and have to be measured from a ship which is neither a steady platform nor is it fixed in position very exactly. The traditional method has been to anchor the ship to provide a "fixed" reference point. In shallow water it is not difficult to anchor, but even here it is not easy to prevent currents or wind from moving the ship relative to its anchor. This movement introduces spurious components into the measured currents. In the open ocean, it is necessary to have special gear to anchor at all in water of several thousands of metres depth, and because the anchor cable cannot be taut the ship is bound to have some movement under the influence of surface currents and wind.

The reason why the anchor cable cannot be taut may need to be explained. An anchor is essentially a device designed to dig into the bottom mud when pulled horizontally, but to break out of the mud when pulled up vertically so that it can be recovered. In ordinary anchoring, in shallow water, the horizontal pull is achieved by using a length or "scope" of cable between ship and anchor which is several times the depth of water. In addition a length of heavy chain between anchor and cable helps to keep the pull on the anchor in the horizontal direction. With this, and a scope of 5 to 7 times the depth, the drag of the anchor on the mud should be sufficient to withstand the pull of the ship due to the effects of wind and current. Reducing the scope may result in the direction of the pull on the anchor rising above the horizontal and the anchor breaking out of the mud. In deep water the scope may be reduced to as little as 1·3 times the water depth but even this leaves the ship with a considerable freedom of movement within a circular area of radius a little less than 0·3 times the water depth. The only way to avoid giving scope to the cable in order to have it taut is to replace the anchor with a heavy weight which sinks into the mud. For a rowboat, a stone small enough for a man to lift may be adequate, but for a deep sea ship the weight required would be too large to handle.

A new technique developed in recent years has been to abandon any attempt to anchor the ship itself but instead to anchor only a buoy in a fixed position and to determine the ship's position continuously relative to the buoy. This is done by means of radar. Any movements of the ship can then be subtracted from currents measured from the ship, leaving the true current. The point is that while it is impractical to anchor a ship with a taut cable it is quite practical to anchor a small buoy by a taut wire so that its horizontal movement is almost eliminated. The buoy is attached by a steel piano wire to a heavy weight on the bottom, rather than an anchor, so that the wire may be taut and the buoy's movement limited. In practice, the main buoy is mounted about 200m below the sea surface to avoid the up-and-down movements associated with the waves. These might strain the wire or lift the weight off the bottom and allow the buoy to drift. A small surface buoy is attached to the main buoy, and serves as a visual and radar marker. An alternative technique is to moor a surface buoy to a bottom weight or anchor by a taut nylon line. This is sufficiently elastic that the up-and-down movements due to waves do not lift the bottom weight. The currents may be measured from the ship by any type of transmitting current meter which indicates both speed and direction. Measurements are made at a sufficient number of depths to obtain an adequate description of the current profile. The weight and wire to the buoy are usually inexpensive and are abandoned after use. The use of this taut-wire position marker buoy has turned out to be a very practical means for enabling current measurements to be made in the open sea. Current meters may also be hung directly from moored buoys.

*Water Sampling Bottles*

In order to determine the properties of a sample of sea-water it is necessary first to obtain the sample. For a "surface" sample, a bucket on a rope often suffices to obtain water for salinity and temperature measurement. A plastic bucket is best, as it is least likely to pollute the sample, and the experienced oceanographer will be found using a small one containing a litre or so rather than a full sized bucket.

For subsurface samples a variety of "water sampling bottles" (Pl. 6 are available. These are generally metal or plastic tubes with either plug valves at each end (Nansen bottle) or spring loaded end caps with rubber washers. The bottle with the ends open is attached to the wire and lowered to the desired depth. There it is closed by the tripping action of a messenger which is slid down the wire. Generally a number of bottles (12 to 18) are attached in series along the wire, at predetermined intervals, and closed in succession. (Each in turn releases a messenger to close the next below it.) When the bottles have been brought back to the deck the water samples are drawn through a tap, following a routine designed to obtain a pure sample. In many designs, the bottle when tripped is released at its upper end and rotates through 180° about a hinge at its lower end where it is clamped to the wire. This is for the purpose of operating the "reversing thermometers" described later, and leads to the bottles being referred to as "reversing water bottles". A capacity of 1·25 litres is common for these bottles but for special purposes, such as $C^{14}$ analysis, larger bottles are used up to several hundred litres capacity.

## Density Measurement

The standard laboratory method, using a weighing bottle, to determine density is not practical at sea because of the motion of the ship, and it is too slow for routine use on shore. The method of weighing a quartz sinker immersed in the water sample has been used by some laboratories. The simple hydrometer is not to be despised for coastal or inshore work where large variations occur, particularly in the surface layers, and high accuracy is not required. Sets of three hydrometers are available to cover the range from 1·000 to 1·031 g/cm³ corresponding to 0 to 41‰ in salinity. This can be determined to about ±0·2‰.

A recent suggestion for the direct measurement of density is to place the water sample in a glass tube which is supported at one end only and to which is attached a piece of metal. The tube is caused to vibrate by passing an alternating electric current through a coil near the metal and the natural frequency of vibration of the tube is determined. This depends on the mass of the tube and contents and hence on the density of the sea-water which is thereby measured. This instrument has the merit of permitting continuous measurement of density if the tube is a U-tube through which the sea-water flows. It is also possible that the method might be adapted to permit the *in situ* measurement of density for which no other practical method is yet available.

Failing adequate means to measure sea-water density accurately and quickly, it is usual to determine it indirectly from salinity and temperature.

## Salinity Measurement

The classical (Knudsen) method of measurement is to determine the chlorinity by titration with standard silver nitrate solution and then to calculate the salinity from the formula given in Chapter 3, In routine use, an accuracy of $\pm 0 \cdot 02\%_0$ is considered reasonable. with rather better accuracy if special care is taken and replicate titrations made. A careful operator may titrate 50 samples per day. It must be remembered that this method is a volumetric one, whereas salinity is defined gravimetrically (i.e. by mass). In consequence it is necessary either to correct for deviations of the temperature of the solutions from the standard, or preferably to carry out the titrations in a temperature controlled room. This titration method is practical but not very convenient to use on board ship.

The determination of salinity through the electrical conductivity measured by means of an a.c. bridge has been in use by the U.S. Coast Guard for the International Ice Patrol in the western North Atlantic since about 1930. The method was not more widely used for many years because of the bulk and expense of the equipment required. This is because the conductivity is as much a function of temperature as of salinity. This necessitates thermostating the samples to $\pm 0 \cdot 001 C°$ during measurement. However, improvements in circuits and equipment encouraged a number of laboratories to bring this method into wider use from about 1956 and an accuracy of $\pm 0 \cdot 003\%_0$ is obtained in routine use. This is very substantially better than the titration method and makes it possible to distinguish water masses which were previously not distinguishable. One of the great advantages of the electrical salinometer is that it uses a null-balance method which is much less tiring for the operator to use than the end-point method of chemical titration. However, the overall bulk of the equipment 1·5 to 2 m³, is inconvenient, and variability in characteristics of the platinum electrodes is still a problem.

In 1957, Esterson of the Chesapeake Bay Institute described an electrical salinometer which avoided the electrode problem by using an inductive (electrodeless) method. Then in 1961, Brown and Hamon in Australia described an inductive salinometer design which has now come into wide use. In this instrument the temperature effect is eliminated not by thermostating the sample but by measuring the temperature while the conductivity is being measured and correcting for its effect automatically in the electrical circuit. The salinity may be measured to an accuracy of $\pm 0.003\%$ over the range from 32 to $39\%$, and with a little practice an operator can determine the salinity of up to 45 samples per hour. The size of the instrument is about $0.06 \, m³ \, (0.6 \times 0.2 \times 0.5 \, m)$ and its weight is only 27 kg wt (Pl. 7).

The refractive index of sea-water is also related to the salinity. The Abbe type of refractometer is not sensitive enough for subsurface ocean salinity measurements but the interference type is. On some of the Soviet oceanographic research vessels this method is apparently used for routine measurement to an accuracy of $\pm 0.02\%$

One feature of all the above methods must be noted—they are all comparative rather than absolute. A so-called "Normal Sea-Water" is prepared in the Laboratoire Océanographique near Copenhagen, Denmark, to an accurately known chlorinity by comparison with a stock of standard sea-water whose chlorinity has been determined gravimetrically. Samples of this Normal Sea-Water sealed in glass ampoules (Pl. 7) are used by oceanographic laboratories throughout the world to standardize the silver nitrate used for titration or to standardize the electrical conductivity bridges. One advantage of this procedure is that all oceanographic laboratories use a common standard for salinity, reducing the possibility of systematic errors occurring and hence making it possible to combine data from different expeditions or surveys in the same area.

The above methods are all laboratory methods. The *in situ* measurement of water properties has always been something to aim for, but has not been achieved for some as yet. Electrode type salinometers have the disadvantage for *in situ* use that a variety of substances and organisms in ocean water tend to cause fouling of the electrodes and consequent change of calibration. The inductive type salinometer is more suitable and several instruments are available or under development. One disadvantage is that the *in situ* sensing element has to be connected to the deck instrument by a multi-core electrical conductor cable which is bulky and requires a special winch with electrical slip-rings if long lengths are to be used.

*Temperature Measurement*

For measuring the temperature of a surface bucket-sample, an ordinary mercury-in-glass thermometer is generally used, taking care not to expose the bucket to the sun (heating) or to the evaporating influence or the wind (cooling).

Another special method coming into use for determining the sea-surface temperature makes use of Stefan's Law that the rate of emission of heat radiation from an object, in this case the sea surface, is proportional to the fourth power of its absolute temperature (see Chapter 5). The radiation is measured by a radiation bolometer which uses a small thermistor as the detecting element. The electrical resistance of the thermistor depends on its temperature which depends on the amount of heat radiation falling on it from the sea. In practice the temperature of the sea is not measured absolutely but is compared with that of a constant-temperature enclosure by placing the thermistor at the focus of a parabolic mirror which is wobbled rapidly so as to look alternately at the sea and at the enclosure. This gives rise to an alternating current proportional to the difference between the two temperatures. This "radiation thermometer" has its chief value in determining the sea temperature from an aircraft. In this application it can be used to examine a

PLATE 1. *C.N.A.V. "Endeavour", a Canadian oceanographic research vessel. (Courtesy Pacific Naval Laboratory, Defence Research Board, Canada.)*

PLATE 2. *Medium duty hydrographic winch, hydraulic drive. (Courtesy Dave Macfarlane.)*

PLATE 3.  *Ekman current meter and spare propellor.*

PLATE 4.  *Remote indicating current meter, (left) sensor with Savonius rotor and direction vane, (right) shipboard indicating unit.*

considerable area of sea in a short time so as to get a nearly simultaneous picture. Strictly speaking, since it operates at long wavelengths (see Chapter 5), it measures the temperature of the surface skin, a fraction of a millimetre thick, of the sea. However, in the presence of wind mixing, it is probable that this does not differ very much from the bulk temperature of the upper mixed layer. A serious source of error with the airborne radiation thermometer is the variability in signal due to the absorption by water drops in the atmosphere between the sea surface and the aircraft. This requires the aircraft to fly at as low an altitude as practicable, i.e. hundreds of metres rather than thousands.

For measuring subsurface temperatures the basic instrument is the "protected reversing thermometer" (Pl. 6) developed especially for oceanographic use. It is a mercury-in-glass thermometer which is attached to the water sampling bottle. When the latter is closed to collect the sample the thermometer is inverted and, as a result of its construction, the mercury "breaks" at a particular point and runs to the other end of the capillary to record the temperature *in situ* at the depth of reversal. The break occurs in the capillary stem above the bulb where a short side arm is placed. It is really rather surprising that the mercury should break as consistently as it does—to better than $\pm 0.01 \text{C}°$ in a good thermometer in laboratory tests. After the thermometer has been reversed it becomes almost insensitive to subsequent changes of temperature and is read when it is brought back on deck. This insensitivity subsequent to reversal is necessary because the surface temperature is usually higher than the deep water temperature and as it was brought back to the surface an ordinary thermometer would warm up and "forget" the deep water temperature. After corrections for scale errors and for the small change in reading due to any difference between the water temperature and that on deck, the reversing thermometer yields the temperature to an accuracy of about $\pm 0.02 \text{C}°$ in routine use.

The "protected" part of its name arises because the thermometer is enclosed in a glass outer case to protect it from the pressure of the water.

4

One way to determine the depth of a water sampling bottle is to use an "unprotected" thermometer (Pl. 6) as well as a protected one The unprotected thermometer has a hole in the glass outer case; as a result the water pressure compresses the glass of the bulb and causes the thermometer to indicate a higher apparent temperature than the protected one. The difference in reading between the two thermometers is a measure of the compression of the glass, which depends on its known compressibility and upon pressure, i.e. on depth. A pair of thermometers, one protected and one unprotected, therefore serves to measure both the temperature *in situ* and the depth, the latter to about $\pm 0.05\%$ of depth or to $\pm 5$ m whichever is the greater.

Another widely used instrument is the "bathythermograph" (Pl. 8) in which a liquid-in-metal thermometer causes a metal point to move in one direction over a smoked glass slide which is itself moved at right angles to this direction by a pressure sensitive metal bellows. The instrument is lowered to its permitted limit in the water (60, 140 or 270 m) and then brought back. Since pressure is directly related to depth, the line scratched on the smoked glass slide forms a graph of temperature against depth. It is read against a calibration grid (Pl. 8) to an accuracy of $\pm 0.2 C°$ and $\pm 2$ m if well calibrated. The great advantage of the bathythermograph is that, although it is less accurate than the reversing thermometer, it gives a continuous trace of temperature against depth instead of only the values at spot depths given by the reversing thermometers.

Development of electrical resistance thermometers is proceeding and experimental instruments with an accuracy of $0.001 C°$ are in use. These record temperature against depth on a chart in the ship's laboratory. Their chief disadvantage is that they require a multi-core electrical conductor cable to connect the sensing head in the water to the laboratory instrument on deck, and consequently a special winch.

A rather sophisticated temperature recorder is the Contouring Temperature Recorder or "Chain" developed by Richardson. This consists of a string of 30 to 40 thermistor temperature-sensitive elements mounted at intervals along a faired cable of 180 to 270 m length. This "Chain" hangs below the ship as it steams along, the weight of the cable itself together with a 1000 kg or more weight at the end helping to keep it close to the vertical even at 5 knots speed. An instrument on deck measures the temperature at each thermistor in turn, interpolates between their values, and draws a continuous graph of whole number temperature values (isotherms) as a function of depth and time along a continuously moving chart. One complaint about the "Chain" is that it collects temperature information in such quantity that it is difficult to find time to analyse it all!

## Radiation Measurement

Direct measurements of $Q_s$ are made with a pyranometer. The sensing element of the Eppley pyranometer consists of two flat plates of copper, one painted with a flat black paint and the other whitened with magnesium oxide. The two plates are placed horizontally with a clear view of the sun and sky and are shielded from draughts by a clear hemispherical cover. The black plate absorbs all radiant energy, short- and long-wave, falling upon it and is thereby heated above the surrounding temperature. The white plate reflects practically all of the energy between 0·3 and 5 $\mu$ (short-wave radiation) but absorbs all long-wave energy. The white plate is consequently heated rather less than the black one and the difference in temperature between them is a measure of the short-wave radiation ($Q_s$) falling on a horizontal surface in the locality of the instrument. The difference in temperature is measured by connecting the "hot" junctions of a group of thermocouples to the black plate and the "cold" junctions to the white plate. The difference in temperature gives rise to a proportional thermoelectric EMF which is measured by a recording galvanometer. The instrument is calibrated by exposing it to a standard source of energy, such as a standard electric filament lamp.

The downward directed component of the long-wave radiation

term $Q_b$ is determined by means of a radiometer. The Gier and Dunkle instrument consists of two horizontal plates of black material separated by a layer of material of known heat conductivity. The upper sheet of black material absorbs all radiation from above falling upon it and is thereby heated above the temperature of the lower sheet. The lower sheet is screened from radiation from below by a sheet of polished metal. The difference in temperature between the upper and the lower sheet is measured by thermocouples and is a measure of the rate at which the sum total of long- and short-wave energy is coming down from above. To determine the value of the long-wave component itself it is necessary to subtract the short-wave radiation rate as measured with a pyranometer. An alternative procedure is to omit the polished metal screen from below the black horizontal plate and arrange the instrument so that the upper plate "looks at" the atmosphere above and the lower plate "looks at" the sea below. In this "net radiometer" arrangement the difference in temperature between the upper and lower plates is a measure of the net amount of radiant energy reaching a horizontal surface, i.e. it is a direct measure of $(Q_s - Q_b)$.

To determine the *transmission of visible light* through the water the simplest device is the Secchi-disc, a white plate about 30 cm in diameter fastened to hang horizontally on the end of a rope marked in metres. The disc is lowered into the sea and the depth at which it is lost to sight is noted. This depth decreases as the absorption coefficient of the sea water increases. In very clear water the depth may be over 50 m, in coastal waters 10 to 2 m, and in some river estuaries less than 1 m. The Secchi-disc is only a semi-quantitative device but being simple it is often used. When one first starts using the device it is rather surprising to find that after very little practice it is possible to obtain consistent readings to better than 10% accuracy, with little variation from individual to individual. The Secchi-disc gives an estimate of the average absorption coefficient $k$ between the surface and the Secchi-disc depth reading $D$. Where the depth $D$ is greater than a few metres it has been shown that $k = 1\cdot7/D$.

A more quantitative instrument for determining the absorption coefficient is called a transparency meter, or a turbidity meter. In this the sensing head which is lowered into the water has a lamp and a photoelectric cell in separate watertight housings mounted 0·5 to 2 m apart. The principle of the instrument is that the current from the photocell is a measure of the amount of light falling upon it. The lamp has a lens and collimator to ensure a parallel beam of light which passes through the water and falls upon the photocell. The light output is kept constant by regulating the current through the lamp. The light beam is usually arranged horizontally because the absorption characteristics in the sea are often horizontally stratified. Also the photocell must not face upward or it would pick up direct sunlight which would give rise to erroneous indications. The photocell is connected by an electrical cable to a microammeter on deck. The current from the photocell is recorded when the sensing head is on deck with the light passing through air whose absorption is taken as zero. In the water the photocurrent decreases due to the absorption of light by the water. The decrease from the air path value is a measure of the absorption by the water. If the photocurrent in air is taken as representative of the initial light intensity $I_o$ and that in water as representative of the intensity $I$ after a path in water of length $x$, the absorption coefficient $k$ may be obtained from the formula $k = 2\cdot3\ (\log I_x - \log I_o)/x$. The length $x$ used in this formula is the length of the water path between the lamp and the photocell.

The instrument is lowered in stages and the absorption coefficient measured at a series of depths to give a vertical profile for this water property. The absorption is often associated with particulate material present in the water independently of its temperature and salinity and therefore the absorption coefficient may be an independent tracer of water movements. The absorption coefficient, or the "turbidity" as it is sometimes called, has been used to distinguish water masses both in the open ocean and in coastal fjords.

Both of the above devices measure the absorption coefficient of the sea-water. For some purposes it is desired to know the amount of light energy $I_z$ which reaches a particular depth $z$. If the light intensity penetrating the surface is known as well as the absorption coefficient at a series of depths, it is possible to calculate how much light will be left at a particular depth. This procedure is rather tedious however, and it is easier to measure the light intensity at the depth directly. This is done by mounting a photocell in a watertight housing to face upward. A microammeter is connected to the cell and is read first with the cell on deck facing upward. This gives a measure of the sun and sky light falling on the sea surface. The cell is then lowered to the depth in which the oceanographer is interested and the photocurrent again measured. The ratio of the photocurrent with the cell in the water to that on deck is then a measure of the ratio of light intensity at depth to that at the surface. If the photocell indications have been calibrated against a standard light-intensity meter then the actual light intensity at depth will be known. It is usual to measure the light intensity at a series of depths below the surface in order to get a more complete record of the distribution of light intensity with depth than would be obtained from a single observation. It is usual also to mount an opal glass or hemisphere in front of the photocell so that it collects light from all directions above its plane.

In the above instruments, the Weston type of photovoltaic cell is used for simplicity (it does not require a separate source of power), because its response to light can be made substantially linear with light intensity, and because it responds over the full range of visible light. (A photocell which responded only to the yellow would show too large an apparent decrease in total light intensity with depth in clear water, whereas one which responded only to the blue and green would show too small a value in the upper layers.) However, the Weston cell has a limited sensitivity and it may be inadequate if measurements are required of the *in situ* light intensity at considerable depths. In this case it is necessary to use the more sensitive photomultiplier type of cell. The disadvantage of this type is that it requires a high voltage supply and precautions have to be taken to avoid electrical leakage when working in sea-water.

## Age of Ocean Water

The term "age" as applied to ocean water means the time since the water mass was last at the surface and in contact with the atmosphere. The importance of this quantity is that it gives some indication of the rate of overturn of ocean water. This is of interest in connection with the rate of replenishment of nutrients in the upper layers and of the use of the ocean basins as places to dump noxious material, particularly radioactive waste. If the average time of overturn is much less than the half-life of such materials it would be dangerous to dump them in the ocean because they would be brought to the surface while still active and might be picked up by fish and so conveyed back to man. We could easily calculate the age of ocean water if we knew the speed of travel of deep currents but this is exactly what we know so little about. For this reason, attempts have been made to develop other methods for determining the age, and some of these will be described.

One method, devised by Worthington, was to use the rate of consumption of dissolved oxygen. He observed that at depths of about 2500 m (in the North Atlantic Deep Water) the average oxygen content decreased by 0·3 ml/l between 1930 and 1950. He attributed the decrease to steady consumption of oxygen by chemical combination with detritus, the rate being 0·3 ml/l ÷ 20 years = 0·015 ml/l/yr. Assuming that the water had been saturated with oxygen when it was last at the surface it would have decreased in oxygen content from its saturation value of 7·6 ml/l at the surface to the 5·8 ml/l observed in 1930. This meant that by 1930 the water had lost 1·8 ml/l of oxygen and, assuming that the rate had been constant at 0·015 ml/l/yr, that the age of the water in 1930 was 1·8 ÷ 0·015 = 120 years. This implied that the water was last at the surface in 1810. This was in a period of very cold climate and Worthington suggests that much of the present North Atlantic Deep Water may have been formed cataclysmically at that time, and that relatively little has been added since. This use of the oxygen consumption to measure the age has been criticized on the grounds that the accuracy of measurement of dissolved oxygen may not be sufficient for the figure of 0·015 ml/l/yr to be very reliable, and on the grounds that the assumption of constant oxygen consumption may be unreal. However, the method is a legitimate attempt to wrest information from the distribution of properties.

Another method, first tried for ocean water in 1950 by Ewing and Kulp, was to use the decay rate of $C^{14}$ in deep waters. It was assumed that the atmosphere at the sea surface was the only source of $C^{14}$ to ocean waters. Away from the surface the $C^{14}$ content would not be replenished and would decay with its half-life of about 5600 years. The early measurements, reported in 1952, suggested an age of the order of 2000 years for water at 2000 to 5000 m in the North Atlantic, but this was subsequently shown to be too high on account of contamination in the chemical processing. More recent reports (1960) from the Lamont Geological Observatory of Columbia University of New York give the following approximate ages, claiming an accuracy of about $\pm 100$ years: North Atlantic Central Water, 600 years; North Atlantic Bottom Water, 900 years; North Atlantic Deep Water, 700 years; Antarctic Intermediate and Bottom Water in the South Atlantic, less than 350 years. (N.B. 'North Atlantic Deep Water', 'Central Water,' etc. are names for distinct water masses in the oceans. They will be described in Chapter 7.)

Measurements by the $C^{14}$ method in the South Pacific have indicated ages of some 1100 to 1900 years in the Deep Water with a suggestion that the time for which the water has been in the Pacific (the "residence time") is about one half of this.

Apart from the experimental uncertainty in the method of measuring the $C^{14}$ activity in a sample of sea-water (a 200 litre sample is needed) there are complications associated with exchange between living and dead matter in the sea and even greater ones resulting from the changes in $C^{14}$ concentration in the atmosphere in the present century. The rapid increase in the use of fossil fuels since about 1900 has reduced the $C^{14}$ concentration in the atmosphere because the $CO_2$ from the fuels contains mostly the stable isotope $C^{12}$, the fuels having been away from the atmosphere for so long. In the opposite direction, since 1954 the effect of nuclear explosions in the atmosphere has been to cause a huge increase in $C^{14}$.

Measurement of the $Sr^{90}$ content of ocean water has revealed significant amounts at depths to 1000 m. As the only source of this isotope is presumed to be the residue from atom bombs, starting in 1954, this indicates that the rate of vertical mixing in the upper waters may be quite rapid.

## PRESENTATION OF DATA

*Vertical Profiles and Sections*

The synoptic oceanographer cannot rely on the distribution of one property alone to determine the full story of the ocean circulation. The discussion in Chapter 7 of the three sections of Fig. 23 will make this apparent. He must use as much independent information as he can obtain, but he must be careful that his interpretation of the circulation is consistent with all the property distributions.

The distribution of properties with depth is best shown on the temperature/depth or salinity/depth *profiles* (e.g. Figs. 8 and 12) which are usually drawn as the first stage in examining oceanographic data. When taking oceanographic stations at sea the oceanographer tries to make observations at standard depths to facilitate comparison between stations. However, the drift of the ship and effects of currents generally cause the oceanographic wire to be at an angle to the vertical and the observations often come out at less than the desired standard depths. If this is the case it is possible to interpolate on the profiles to get values at the required depths. A more sophisticated way to do this is to feed the "raw" or "observed" data into a computer which has been programmed to interpolate between the observed points according to some standard mathematical procedure and to give out the values at the required standard depths. The computer is often programmed to do more than this. Not only does it interpolate for the desired depth but the output typewriter prepares a complete master sheet with observed and interpolated data, and assembles station position, date, meteorological data, etc., in a standard format ready to be duplicated for the data report which is one of the first products of an oceanographic cruise. This data report is simply a list of the numerical values for the observations made at sea, corrected for instrument errors, etc., but without any attempt made to interpret them.

Vertical profiles are one way of displaying the data for a single station but if other parameters enter, such as time or range of geographical position, it is necessary to use further displays. For example, in Fig. 9a are presented vertical profiles of temperatures at a fixed station for a number of months. The variation of temperature as a function of time is then shown in two ways in Figs. 9b and 9c. These plots have been discussed in Chapter 4.

The horizontal *sections* of properties such as those of Figs. 6, 7 and 11 or the vertical ones of Figs. 23, 24 and 29 are most useful in displaying the geographic distributions of individual properties. They are not generally used to show the interdependence of the properties because it is difficult to show more than two properties simultaneously on one diagram, even using multiple colours. Even with only two properties, the relations between them cannot be appreciated as well, for instance, as on the characteristic diagrams described below.

## Characteristic Diagrams

Although one can plot separate vertical profiles and sections of temperature, salinity, dissolved oxygen, etc., one must be careful not to consider these properties to be independent in the ocean. Physically the quantities are independent of each other in the sense that in a sample of sea-water it is possible to alter the value of any one without altering the others. (Note that density is not included in the above list because it is dependent on temperature and salinity.) However, observations indicate that oceanographically the properties do not occur in all possible combinations. The reason for this is that most ocean water masses acquire their characteristic properties at the surface of the sea in particular localities. The water properties are determined there by the local climate, and when the water sinks along density surfaces it carries the properties with it. The result is that instead of all possible combinations of temperature, salinity, oxygen, etc., occurring in the ocean, we find that only a limited number of particular combinations occur. In consequence, we can often recognize a water mass by its characteristic combination of water properties.

To show these combinations, it is usual to plot "characteristic diagrams" of the water properties. Helland-Hansen in 1918 was the first to demonstrate this technique by plotting temperature against salinity for each individual oceanographic station, in addition to the separate plots of temperature, salinity, etc., against depth. Figures 21 and 22 contain average examples for the main oceans. They will be referred to further in Chapter 7. Each point on the $[TS]$ plot represents the temperature and salinity of the water at one depth in the vertical column at the oceanographic station. The points are then joined together in order of depth by a smooth (but generally not straight) line which is called the $[TS]$ diagram for that station. Other characteristic diagrams such as $[TO_2]$ $[SO_2]$, $[T, \text{phosphate}]$, etc., may also be plotted.

It is not necessary to plot $[T, density]$ diagrams because density depends on temperature and salinity and therefore automatically appears on the $[TS]$ diagram. Each point on this diagram corresponds to a particular combination of temperature and salinity and therefore to a particular density. However, the same density may be attained by different combinations of temperature and salinity, and these combinations lie on a smooth curve on the $[TS]$ plotting sheet and can be drawn in as shown by the full lines on Fig. 2.

When discussing the $[TS]$ diagram, a water body which is represented by a point is called a water "type", whereas one represented by a line is called a water "mass". These are ideal definitions. In practice the points on a $[TS]$ plot representing a water "type" would have a small scatter about the ideal point, while the points representing a water "mass" would have some scatter about an ideal line. Climatic processes at the surface tend to form water types; a water mass results from the mixing of two or more water types. For instance, in Fig. 2 the straight dotted line $AB$ represents a water mass made up of mixtures in various proportions of water types $A$ and $B$. The curved dashed line $AC$ represents a mass made up of mixtures of types $A$, $B$ and $C$ in different proportions. This interpretation implies that temperature and salinity are conservative quantities in the ocean, i.e. that no processes exist for generating heat or salt or for removing them. This is the case within the body of the ocean, but near the surface it is not so. Here, the sun may heat the water or evaporation cool it, rain may decrease the salinity or evaporation increase it. Therefore in plotting the $[TS]$ diagram it is usual to regard the points corresponding to shallow depths within the influence of the surface effects as less conservative, or even to omit them altogether.

The $[TS]$ diagram turns out to be a powerful tool for the study of ocean waters. The shape of the diagram is often characteristic of water from a particular locality in the ocean, and individual features of the diagram may indicate mixtures of different types of water. For example, considering the Atlantic water masses, the $[TS]$ diagram of Fig. 21 shows most clearly what average values of temperature and salinity are found in the Atlantic and what combinations. It also indicates the existence of salinity minima and maxima, such as those of the Antarctic Intermediate and of the North Atlantic Deep Waters respectively.

Salinity maxima or minima (such as $C$ or $B$ in Fig. 15a) are common on $[TS]$ diagrams but, except for the surface and bottom values, temperature maxima or minima are uncommon. The reason is that except in polar or coastal regions, density depends chiefly on temperature and less on salinity. A temperature maximum such as $G$ in Fig. 15b would imply that the water above the level of $G$ (i.e. toward $F$) was denser than that at $G$. Or a temperature minimum as at $F$ would imply that the water below it (i.e. toward $G$) was less dense than that at $F$. Both of these situations are unstable in the ocean and are only found under exceptional circumstances, such as temporarily in the presence of eddies in the complicated waters at the northern side of the Gulf Stream where the Labrador Current joins it.

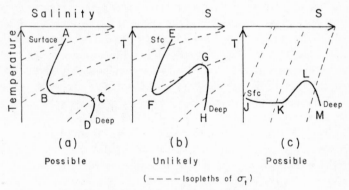

Fig. 15. *Schematic temperature/salinity diagrams.*

On the other hand, in polar regions where the salinity and temperature are both low the density depends chiefly on the salinity· Under these conditions the isopleths of $\sigma_t$ on the [$TS$] diagram are more nearly parallel to the temperature axis (e.g. Fig. 15c) and a temperature minimum ($K$) or maximum ($L$) is quite possible since the density increases continuously from the surface to the deep water.

The [$TS$] diagram is also useful for checking data to determine if the individual points are in error. If a point lies well off the expected curve for a particular region one tends to regard it with suspicion.

Tongue-like distributions of water properties in the vertical plane are very helpful in indicating the direction of movement of the water. Wüst developed the "core method" as a technique for determining water flow in the ocean. A "core" is defined as a region where a water property reaches a maximum or minimum value within a tongue-like distribution, e.g. the salinity minimum of the Antarctic Intermediate Water shown in Fig. 23. A vertical profile of the water property is used to detect such a core which is taken as the centre of the flow. A core gradually weakens along its length as a result of mixing with the surrounding water. A [TS] diagram may be plotted for a series of water samples taken along the core from its start, usually at the region of formation of the water type at the surface, to its end where it can no longer be detected. The point on the diagram representing the original water type represents 100% concentration and the end point represents 0% concentration of the original type. The position of any point on the [TS] line then represents the proportion of original water remaining by its proportionate distance from the end point.

The [TS] diagram however suffers from two disadvantages. One is that it gives a poor indication of the distribution in depth of the different water masses because the depth scale along the [TS] curve is not linear. For this reason it is not practical to interpolate for temperature or salinity values on the [TS] diagram except very roughly. The other disadvantage of the [TS] diagram is that it gives no indication of the geographic distribution of the water masses. This is better done on horizontal or vertical sections.

An interesting adaptation of the [TS] diagram was developed by Montgomery and used by him and his colleagues to display the distribution of temperature and salinity of the ocean waters in proportion to their volume. Essentially a [TS] plotting sheet was divided into a grid of squares of dimensions, say 2C° by 1‰. On each square was entered the volume of water whose temperatures and salinity values lay within those of the square. For this purpose the potential temperature (see Chapter 3) was used rather than the *in situ* temperature. The volume information was arrived at from observed oceanographic data in the following manner. Oceanographic stations were selected for which the measurements of water properties extended from the surface to the bottom. The stations were as evenly spaced as possible and each was taken to represent a horizontal area around it so that the sum total of all the station areas was equal to the total area of the region being considered. At each station, the temperature and salinity observed at each depth were taken to represent the layer of water extending from half-way to the observation above to half-way to the observation below. The product of this interval of depth with the horizontal area represented by the station gave the volume of water for which the particular values of temperatures and salinity were representative. This volume was entered in the appropriate grid square on the $[TS]$ diagram. This procedure was carried out for all the temperature/salinity values for all the stations and then the volumes in each square were totalled. The final result was a gridded diagram in which the number in each square showed the volume of water having the temperature and salinity values of that square. It will be called a $[TSV]$ diagram. On a typical such diagram, some squares have large volumes and many have none at all.

As an example of the result, a $[TSV]$ diagram for the Atlantic and adjacent seas is shown as Fig. 16a. This figure is simplified slightly from Montgomery's original diagram and the unit of volume is $10^5 \text{km}^3$. The number on each square then shows the number of these units of volume of water which have the temperature and salinity within the range of that square. It is seen that the water properties are by no means uniformly distributed but that there is a concentration of volume near 2°C and 35‰. This North Atlantic Deep Water, with a volume of $1600 \times 10^5 \text{km}^3$, is seen to occupy a large proportion of the total volume of the Atlantic which is about $3528 \times 10^5 \text{km}^3$. The Antarctic Bottom Water and the Arctic Deep have much the same characteristics and fall in the same square on the diagram with a combined volume of $366 \times 10^5 \text{km}^3$. Two other distinctive water masses are the Mediterranean Water with characteristically high salinity and temperature, and the Black Sea Water with low salinity.

The numbers outside the axes of the diagram are the sums of the volume numbers in the horizontal rows and in the vertical columns respectively on the diagram. Down the right hand side, this series of numbers shows that the great bulk (85%) of the Atlantic water has a salinity between 34 and 35‰. In temperature, 47% of the Atlantic water is between 2° and 4°C and 76% is between −2° and 4°C.

It will be noted that in Fig. 16, following Montgomery's original arrangement, the temperature and salinity scales have been rotated 90° compared to the conventional arrangement (e.g. Fig. 21), and salinity increases downward. This means that the most dense water on Fig. 16 will appear at the bottom left hand corner, and the least dense at the top right. The dashed lines are isopleths of thermosteric anomaly ($\delta_T$, Chapter 3).

Figure 16a is an example of a coarse scale $[TSV]$ diagram. Fine scale diagrams have also been prepared with grid squares of $0.5\,C°$ and $0.1‰$ side to show more detail of the water mass volumes.

Similar diagrams have been combined to show the $[TSV]$ characteristics of the world ocean (Fig. 16b). Montgomery points out that the mean values calculated from these 1957 statistics do not differ significantly from values determined by Krümmel in 1907. One of the chief reasons for the small differences between Krümmel's averages based on few data and Montgomery's based on many more is the small range of temperatures and salinity found in the bulk of the oceans. The oceanographic "climate" is so uniform below the surface layer that comparatively few observations sufficed to enable Krümmel to make a good estimate of the mean values. It must not be concluded, however, that little had been gained in oceanographic knowledge between 1907 and 1957. Mean values conceal much detail, and the very fact that deep water characteristics in the ocean have a small range of values makes it difficult for the synoptic oceanographer to distinguish one water mass from another. In fact, the development in recent years of the electrical conductivity salinometer with its increased sensitivity has helped a great deal to

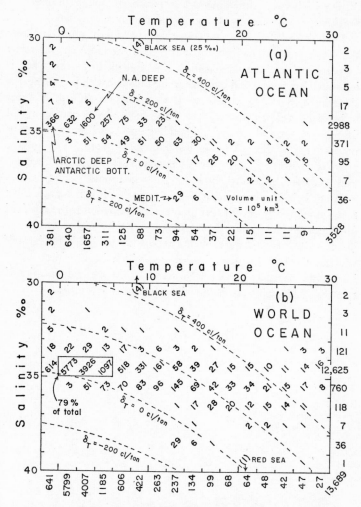

Fig. 16.  *Temperature/salinity/volume diagrams for the Atlantic and the World Ocean (after Montgomery).*

distinguish between different water masses, even though the increased sensitivity is not likely to reveal any change in mean values.

There is one limitation in presenting a $[TSV]$ diagram. It shows the relations between three quantities and therefore should really be presented in three dimensions. It is difficult to do this when it is printed on paper, and one has to be satisfied with indicating the third quantity, $V$, by numbers. It would not be difficult however to build up a three dimensional $[TSV]$ model by preparing a grid for temperature and salinity and building up on each square columns proportional to the volume of water in that square. The volume of water of North Atlantic Deep characteristics would then become very apparent, towering above all other columns.

From the above remarks, it will be seen that it is not practicable to recommend any one form of graphical presentation as the standard for oceanographic data. An oceanographer who wishes to present his data and his analysis of it in a report has to decide for himself which form best displays the features which he considers to be important. He may well have to use all of the methods mentioned to make all his points, or he may have to invent new ones.

# CHAPTER SEVEN

# Circulation and Water Masses of the Oceans

WE NOW come to the circulation of the oceans, first discussing some of the general features of the main ocean circulations and then proceeding to describe the circulation and character of the water masses in the individual oceans.

## GENERAL

It must be stressed that in one way or another the energy from the sun's radiation is responsible for these circulations. In fact, both the atmospheric and the oceanic circulations are driven by this energy and we should perhaps really study both together. As this book is primarily about the ocean we will concentrate on the water circulation but it will be apparent that the atmosphere plays a considerable part in driving the water currents.

The ocean circulation can be divided into two parts, the thermohaline and the wind-driven components. Another way to describe these is to say that the ocean circulation is in part due to changes in density caused by climatic changes and in part due to the wind stress. The manner in which these factors determine the circulation is discussed in *Dynamical Oceanography* and all that will be done here will be to describe the processes in qualitative fashion.

The term *thermohaline circulation* is used to refer to the movement of water that takes place when its density its changed by change of temperature or of salinity in a suitable part of its bulk. A standard laboratory demonstration of thermal circulation is to take a large beaker of water and heat it at the bottom by means of a bunsen burner. The water which is heated expands and rises (convection) as a consequence of Archimedes' Principle. A few crystals of potassium permanganate or dye dropped into the water will dissolve and colour the bottom water and show it rising over the source of heat and sinking elsewhere. The sinking in this case is simply a consequence of continuity of volume. In the case of the atmosphere the sun's energy is absorbed by the land, this heats the air near to it and a similar circulation to that in the beaker takes place. Cumulus clouds developing on a summer day often reveal where the upward flow of this kind of circulation is taking place.

The laboratory experiment with the beaker of water and the heating of the atmosphere have this in common—the heat is supplied at the bottom of the fluid. The situation is different in the ocean in that the sun's heat is supplied at the top; this makes a great deal of difference. A liquid warmed at its top surface cannot rise and therefore a circulation does not develop. If we were to take a long tank of water and heat the surface at one end, then some motion would occur. The heated water would expand and raise the water surface slightly at this end. The warmed surface water would then flow toward the cold end over the top of the cold water but no circulation in the full sense would develop. Some of the early theories of the ocean circulation ascribed the currents to a thermal flow of this sort. The stronger heating of the sea near the equator was recognized and it was suggested that the water then flowed north and south toward the poles. While it is possible that the differential heating between the equatorial and the polar regions may have some effect of this nature it is now believed to be a minor one.

Since there is no significant source of heat to the bottom of the oceans a thermal circulation like that in the beaker and in the atmosphere plays little part in the ocean circulation.

However, heating at the equator is only one part of the heat budget. It has already been shown that there is a net loss of heat energy from the oceans at high latitudes. The result of the cooling of the water is an increase in density which may be sufficient to cause it to sink and so displace the deeper water. The thermohaline circulation of the oceans is due to increase of density at the upper surface, either directly by cooling or indirectly when ice freezes out and increases the salinity. In the North Atlantic the cooling effect in the winter is considered to be responsible for the sinking of water from the surface to considerable depths. In the Antarctic, the freezing effect is important. The sea-ice will not be pure ice, as some salt is usually trapped among the ice crystals, but it is usually less saline than the sea-water from which it was formed. The remaining sea-water is therefore more saline and more dense than before, and this will cause it to sink. One may summarize then by stating that a characteristic of the thermohaline circulation is that it originates as a vertical flow sinking to mid-depth or even to the ocean bottom, followed by horizontal flow.

An increase of salinity may also occur due to evaporation in the tropics but generally this is accompanied by solar heating at the same time and the decrease in density due to heating prevails over the increase due to evaporation. The more saline water stays at the surface. Evaporation is therefore not a direct factor in causing water to sink but it does act indirectly as will be described for the Mediterranean and the Red Sea.

The *wind driven circulation* is principally in the upper few hundreds of metres and therefore is primarily a horizontal circulation in contrast to the thermohaline one. In *Dynamical Oceanography* the mechanism is described by which the wind blowing over the sea surface causes the water to move. Here we will just accept this as a consequence of fluid friction, but note that the direction of motion of the water in the open ocean is not the same as that of the wind. The rotation of the earth gives rise to the Coriolis force which results in the wind driven currents in the upper, wind-mixed layer in the open sea moving in a direction to the right of the wind direction in the northern hemisphere and to the left in the southern.

The ocean currents are then a result of the combined effects of the thermohaline motions and of the wind driven ones. The former probably prevail in the deep water while the latter prevail in the upper layers. In both cases, the motion usually continues far beyond the place where it was initiated, just as water may be made to circulate round a hand basin by blowing along the surface at one side only.

When one attempts to describe the *circulation* and *water* masses of the oceans of the world one is faced with a problem. If one wishes to present the details one can only do so for a region of limited extent and so one must divide up the world ocean into regions for this purpose. In practice, this is not too difficult to do; the oceans almost divide themselves into regions. For instance the Atlantic can be described regionally as the North, the Equatorial and the South Atlantic, together with the adjacent seas such as the Mediterranean, the Labrador Sea, etc. A professional oceanographer who is studying a particular region for a particular purpose, e.g. as part of a study of the fisheries, will be concerned with the details in that region. But almost inevitably when he selects a particular area for study he finds that the waters within the region are influenced by waters without the region, e.g. by currents entering the area of study from elsewhere. Then to understand the particular area he has to extend his study beyond the area, and sometimes it is difficult to stop this extension before reaching the boundary shores of the ocean itself. In other words, to understand the part one must understand the whole.

Since the present book is intended only as an introduction to Descriptive Oceanography, and since the total volume of detailed data available is far too great to include or even summarize within its pages, the main endeavour in the following description will be to acquaint the reader with the main features of the ocean circulations and water masses, with some description of details for a few areas as examples. It is hoped that this approach will provide him with enough feeling for the character of the ocean circulation and water masses as a whole, that he will have sufficient background to study smaller areas in detail later on.

Again, when describing the circulations and the water masses one is faced with the question of which to present first. It is the old problem of "which came first, the chicken or the egg?" In this book the author has decided to take the operational approach. For the upper waters, the circulation will be described first. The reason for doing this is that we have a good deal of direct information about the circulation of the upper layers, but the movements of the deep waters are largely inferred from the distributions of properties.

For the surface-layer, ten or so metres thick, there is a body of information available on currents over a considerable proportion of the oceans. This information has been obtained as a by-product of ship navigation. A ship which maintains a set course with reference to a compass and a set speed by using a particular engine speed will not necessarily travel on that particular course or at that particular speed relative to the solid earth. The reason is that the currents of the ocean will add vectorially to the ship's velocity resulting in a difference between the course steered and the speed of the ship through the water and the course and speed actually made good. By making a vector subtraction of the ship's velocity from the actual velocity it is possible to determine the current velocity, i.e. its speed and its direction. Maury, of the U.S. Navy Hydrographic Office, initiated the collection of such current data from ship's logs and this information has continued to be collected and collated over the years. The information is published regularly by the Hydrographic Office in the form of Pilot Charts of the various oceans; other national authorities have accumulated and published similar information. The result is that we now have a knowledge of the surface circulation of much of the oceans. This knowledge is substantial and detailed in the regions much travelled by ships, such as the main traffic routes across the North Atlantic and the North Pacific, but is scanty in other regions such as the eastern South Pacific and the southern Indian Ocean. As has already been stated the upper layer circulation is driven by the winds and from the results of studies in dynamical oceanography we can obtain from the surface layer circulation a very good idea of the whole upper layer circulation down to the thermocline. There-fore, in describing the upper layers of the oceans, the circulation will be described first and the water properties second. This is a logical order since the upper water properties are chiefly determined by the history of the water, i.e. where it has been carried by the current.

For the deep water, the water mass characteristics will be described first and then the movements, since most of our knowledge of the deep water circulation has been obtained by interpretation of the distributions of properties. In addition to the deep water flows having been inferred from the property distributions the flows are mostly driven by the distribution of density which in itself is determined by the distribution of temperature and salinity. Only in recent years has the invention by Swallow of the neutrally buoyant float permitted satisfactory direct observations of the deep water movements. To date, the information available from this source is limited in amount and is only from a few regions.

Some indication of what is meant by "upper" and "deep" waters must be given before going further. It is not easy to give an exact figure for the thickness of the *upper water* but it is usually taken to extend from the sea surface to the depth at which the decrease in temperature with depth becomes small. This may be between 300 and 1000m. The upper layer contains the surface or mixed layer of 50 to 200m depth in which most of the seasonal variations of properties occur and which is usually fairly homo-geneous due to mixing by the action of the waves caused by the wind. The remainder of the upper layer is usually well stratified and stable, and includes the thermocline. The *deep water* includes all that below the upper water, and is less stable than the latter. If the layer in contact with the bottom has properties distinct from those of the deep water above, it is referred to as the "bottom" water.

Before proceeding to the more detailed description of the ocean areas, the main features will be presented briefly so that the reader may appreciate how the details fit into the whole. The *circulations in the major ocean areas* show considerable similarities; the differences are largely in detail. In the upper layer there is a major clockwise circulation or "gyre" in both the North Atlantic and the North Pacific and a counter-clockwise gyre in the southern parts of the Atlantic, Pacific and Indian Oceans. In the North Atlantic and Pacific a very conspicuous feature is that the currents are narrower and swifter on the west side of each ocean than elsewhere (westward intensification of the currents). There is evidence of the same phenomenon in the South Atlantic and the Indian Ocean but the western South Pacific circulation is rather complex and the intensification is not clear. In the equatorial regions of all three oceans there are similar current systems consisting of a westward flowing South Equatorial Current at or south of the equator and a westward flowing North Equatorial Current further north. In the Pacific these two are separated by an eastward flowing Equatorial Counter Current across the full width of the ocean; in the Atlantic the Counter Current is only significant in the eastern part. In the Indian Ocean the three current pattern is present for part of the year. Defant calls these equatorial current systems the "backbone of the circulation" to emphasize our present belief that the northern and southern gyres are driven mainly by the trade winds in low latitudes. The facts that the regions maintain their identity of circulation and of water mass characteristics indicate that the climatic processes which determine them must be continuing to act.

In the deep water the major flows are north and south, not necessarily evenly distributed across the widths of the oceans but probably being stronger on the west sides.

The two polar regions show marked differences which are due in part to the differences in character of the driving forces but principally to the difference in topography of the two basins.

Since the Southern Ocean is openly connected with the other main oceans, and water which acquires its characteristics here has a profound influence on the deep waters in the other oceans we will start with this region.

## SOUTHERN OCEAN

The Southern Ocean has the land mass of the Antarctic continent to form a southern boundary but has no land boundary to its north and is continuous with the other major oceans. However, the surface waters of the region have well defined characteristics whose isopleths run roughly parallel to lines of latitude, and features of these characteristics are used to define the northern boundary of the Southern Ocean. Going north from the Antarctic continent the average sea surface temperature increases slowly until a region is reached where a relatively rapid increase of 2 to 3C° occurs. The surface water from south of the region of rapid temperature increase is moving north and sinks when it reaches the region, continuing north below the surface. At the surface therefore the water is converging to this region which is known as the Antarctic Convergence (Fig. 17). Continuing north from this Convergence the temperature rises slowly to a second region where it rises rapidly by about 4C° and the salinity by about 0·5‰. This is referred to as the Subtropical Convergence (Fig. 17).

The Antarctic Convergence is found at about 50°S in the Atlantic and Indian Oceans and at about 60°S in the Pacific (Fig. 17). The Subtropical Convergence is at about 40°S round most of the Antarctic but its position has not been well determined in the eastern South Pacific which is a poorly known region oceanographically. The two convergences divide the surface waters of the Southern Ocean into two zones, the Antarctic zone from the continent to the Antarctic Convergence, and the Subantarctic zone from there to the Subtropical Convergence (Fig. 18). In the Antarctic zone, the surface temperature is between −1·9° and 1°C in winter and between −1° and 4°C in summer, while in the Subantarctic zone it is between 4° and 10°C in winter and up to 14°C in summer. (Note that unless a minus sign is placed before a temperature it is understood to be positive.) Although in this definition the surface temperature distribution has been used to locate the convergences, it is found that other water characteristics support this zonation.  Also the subsurface characteristics show a marked homogeneity around the Antarctic within these regions.

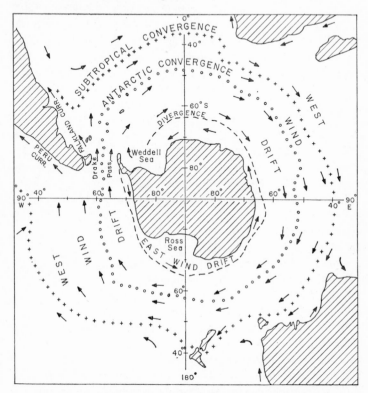

FIG. 17. *Southern Ocean—surface circulation and mean positions of the Antarctic and Subtropical Convergences* (*Adapted from Deacon, "Discovery" Reports, by permission*).

The *circulation* in the Southern Ocean has the following features. In a narrow zone round most of the continent there is a westward flowing coastal current, called by Deacon the "East Wind Drift" because it is attributed to the prevailing easterly winds off the coast.   Outside this zone the Southern Ocean waters move in a grand circulation round the continent from west to east (Fig. 17). The entire eastward circulation is referred to as the "Circumpolar Current", and the surface circulation as the "West Wind Drift".

At this point attention is drawn to the difference between the manners in which wind directions and water current directions are stated.  It is usual to express wind direction as where the wind comes *from*, i.e. the westerly winds blow from west to east.  This convention possibly results from sailing ship experience in which one is more conscious of where the wind and weather are coming from than where they are going to.   For water currents, however, it is usual to state the direction *toward* which the water is flowing, i.e. the easterly Circumpolar Current flows to the east.

The surface current is due largely to the frictional stress of the westerly wind, giving rise to the name "West Wind Drift" (Fig. 17). (The westerly wind in the Southern Ocean was notorious in sailing ship days and, together with the current, made it difficult for such vessels to get round Cape Horn from the Atlantic to the Pacific.) In addition, the Coriolis force contributes to cause a northward component of motion which gives rise to the Antarctic Convergence. Below the wind-driven layer, the circumpolar circulation is closely associated with the distribution of density as is described in *Dynamical Oceanography*.

In its circuit round the continent the Circumpolar Current is obstructed only in the narrow Drake Passage between South America and the Palmer Peninsula projecting north from Antarctica.   The Circumpolar Current is not a very fast one, only about 4 cm/sec in the Antarctic zone and increasing to 15 cm/sec north of the Antarctic Convergence and then decreasing again toward the Subtropical Convergence.   However the current is very deep and its volume transport was estimated by Sverdrup as up to 150 million m³/sec, and more recently by Soviet oceanographers as up to 190 million m³/sec, making it the mightiest current in the oceans. (The most commonly used unit for volume transport is "one million m³/sec"— for the sake of brevity hereafter this will be referred to as "one sverdrup", following the recent suggestion by Dunbar. The above volume transports would then be written as 150sv and 190sv respectively.) This current shows some variations in direction as it flows round the continent and there is evidence that some of these are due to the effects of the submarine topography.   Some of the current branches off and flows north between Australia and New Zealand at subsurface levels and some, including surface water, flows north as the Peru Current up the west coast of South America into the South Pacific (Fig. 17), making significant contributions to the circulation and water masses of that ocean. There is some flow from the Current northward into the Atlantic between South America and the Falkland Islands as the Falkland Current (Fig. 17).

The *water masses* of the Southern Ocean have typical high latitude characteristics.  The Antarctic Surface Water has properties which are determined by ice melting in summer and by cooling in winter. This layer of about 100 to 250 m thickness has a salinity of less than 34·5‰ and a low temperature ranging down to the freezing point at that salinity, about −1·9°C. The temperatures are lowest at the south and increase toward the north due to absorption of heat during the summer.  It must be remembered that in the polar regions, south or north, an effect of sea-ice is to limit the range of temperature variation between summer and winter. The reason lies in the large value of the latent heat of melting of ice.  In one direction, the freezing point of sea-water at the salinities found at high latitudes is no lower than −1·9°C and limits the reduction of temperature which can occur in the water. In the other direction, the melting of ice requires a considerable proportion of the heat inflow during the summer, leaving only a small part to raise the temperature of the water.

Below the surface and extending to the bottom at depths to 4000 m is the Antarctic Circumpolar Water. Its temperature in the Antarctic zone rises to a maximum of about 1·5 to 2·5°C at 300 to 600 m and then decreases to 0 to 0·5°C at the bottom. Its mean salinity is close to 34·7‰. These characteristic properties are found all round the Antarctic continent at the same depths.

A very important water mass is the Antarctic Bottom Water.

It is formed in the Weddell Sea, a large bay on the Atlantic side of the Antarctic continent (Fig. 17). This water is a mixture of Antarctic Circumpolar Water with Shelf Water which has attained its properties on the continental shelf region of the Weddell Sea. The Shelf Water has a temperature of $-1 \cdot 9°C$ and a salinity of $34 \cdot 6‰$. Its density ($\sigma_t$) of $27 \cdot 9$ is among the highest found in the southern oceans. (Values as high as $27 \cdot 96$ are found in the Ross Sea.) The mixing with Circumpolar Water reduces its density to slightly below $27 \cdot 9$ as it flows out from the Weddell Sea. Because of this high density it flows down the continental slope into the South Atlantic (Fig. 18) and also eastward through the Indian and Pacific sectors of the Southern Ocean. The eastward flow round the continent is deduced from the continuity of the temperature and salinity values together with the steady decrease in oxygen content from the Atlantic sector through the Indian and Pacific sectors. If we knew the rate at which oxygen is used up in the water it would be possible to estimate the speed of flow from the rate of decrease of oxygen. Unfortunately we do not have any reliable figures for the oxygen consumption in this region.

In the Subantarctic region the water masses become more numerous. Some of them originate in the Southern Ocean but others originate outside and information which will be given later in this chapter has been used to identify them. In addition, the upper water masses show some differences between the Atlantic, Indian and Pacific sectors of the Southern Ocean in contrast to the relatively uniform character of the Antarctic upper water.

The Subantarctic Upper Water occupies the upper 500 m or so and has a temperature of 4 to 10°C in the winter and up to 14°C in summer, and a salinity from $33 \cdot 9$ to $34 \cdot 9‰$ in winter and as low as $33‰$ in summer as ice melts. The lowest temperatures and salinities are found in the Pacific sector and the highest in the Atlantic sector. This Upper Water has a southward component of motion which accounts for its higher temperature than the waters farther south. A salinity maximum is also present in all sectors at 150 to 450 m depth.

Below this water is the Antarctic Intermediate Water which includes surface water from the Antarctic zone and is formed by mixing below the surface at and north of the Antarctic Conver-

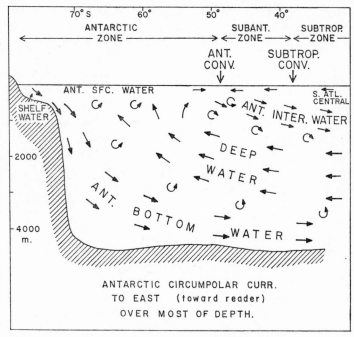

FIG. 18.  *Vertical components of the circulation in the Atlantic sector of the Southern Ocean. (Adapted by permission from Deacon, "Discovery" Reports, and Sverdrup, Johnson and Fleming, The Oceans, their Physics, Chemistry and General Biology, (C) 1942 by Prentice-Hall Inc., Englewood Cliffs, N.J.)*

gence. It continues northward with some admixture from the Upper Water (Fig. 18). The Intermediate Water has a thickness of about 500 m at the northern limit of the Subantarctic region, under the Subtropical Convergence. It is more homogeneous in properties than the Upper Water, with a temperature of about 2°C and a salinity of 33·8‰. It sinks because its density $(\sigma_t)$ of 27·0 is greater than that of the water to its north. As it flows to the north it mixes with more saline water above and below it and its salinity rises gradually. The Antarctic Intermediate Water flowing north forms a tongue of relatively low salinity water with its centre at 800 to 1000 metres depth at 40° S and to the north of this (see Fig. 23). The water also has a relatively high oxygen content of 5 to 7 ml/l since it has only recently left the surface.

The next water mass below is the Deep Water which moves with a southward component of motion in addition to its eastward circulation as a part of the Circumpolar Current (Fig. 18). It lies between 1500 and 3000 m depth in the Subantarctic region and has a temperature of 2 to 3°C and a salinity of 34·6 to 34·8‰. It is sometimes referred to as the "warm" deep water. In a vertical profile and in the $[TS]$ diagram (Fig. 21a) the water does show as a very slight temperature maximum but it is only warm relative to the colder Intermediate and Bottom water. It was first observed in 1821 but only recognized as being of North Atlantic origin by Merz and Wüst in 1922. The Upper Deep Water shows a salinity maximum in the Atlantic and Indian sectors, while the Lower Deep Water is difficult to distinguish from the Antarctic Circumpolar Water. In the Pacific, the Upper Deep Water is less easy to distinguish from the Antarctic Circumpolar Water than in the other ocean sectors. The Deep Water has a southward component of motion, contrary to the Intermediate Water above it and to the Bottom Water below. There is inevitably some mixing between them, and the waters above and below are both modified by mixing with the Deep Water. In moving south from the Atlantic the Deep Water rises toward the surface (Fig. 18). It is probable that it does not actually reach the surface as a water mass but diverges north and south, mixing with surface water and contributing to the Antarctic Intermediate Water and to the Bottom Water. The Deep Water comes from the North Atlantic and has been away from the surface for a long time; it has a low oxygen content and high concentrations of the so-called nutrients, phosphate, nitrate,

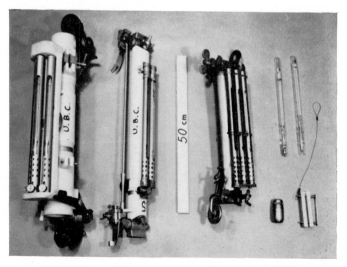

PLATE 5.  *Meter wheel.*

PLATE 6.  *Water sampling bottles (N.I.O., Nansen and Fjarlie), protected and unprotected reversing thermometers, and messengers.*

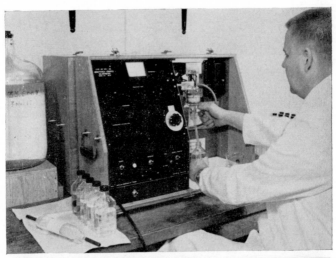

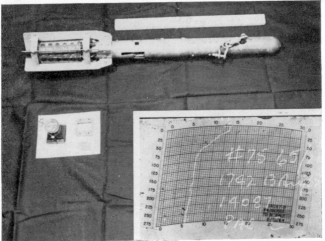

PLATE 7. *Inductive salinometer, (bottom left) ampoule of "Normal Sea-Water".*

PLATE 8. *(top) Bathythermograph, (left) viewer, calibration grid and slide, (right) slide as seen against grid.*

etc., which are needed for plant growth. This continual supply of nutrients is one of the reasons for this region being prolific in plant growth and consequently in zooplankton. The latter forms a source of food in the sea and the large whaling industry is one consequence. In a vertical profile of water properties the Deep Water is characterized by an oxygen minimum as it lies between the Intermediate and Bottom waters, both of which were more recently at the surface and consequently are richer in oxygen.

The deepest water in the Subantarctic region is the Bottom Water flowing north from the Antarctic (Fig. 18). Mixing with the overlying Deep Water its temperature is raised to $0.3°$ to $1.5°C$ and its salinity to $34.7$ to $34.8\%_{00}$.

Summarizing, it is possible to divide the Southern Ocean into two zonal regions round the continent, an Antarctic zone nearer to the land and a Subantarctic zone farther north. In the former, there is a thin surface layer of cold Antarctic Surface Water of relatively low salinity from summer melting of ice. Below this there is the large mass of the Antarctic Circumpolar Water of uniform properties all round the continent. The cold Antarctic Bottom Water formed in the Weddell Sea flows north and east into the three large oceans. In the Subantarctic zone there are four distinct water masses. The Subantarctic Upper Water is warmer and more saline than the Antarctic Surface water. Below this the Antarctic Intermediate Water is fed by Antarctic Surface Water flowing north and descending beneath the Upper Water. Below this again is the large body of Deep Water flowing south and rising over the Antarctic Bottom Water which flows north. The Intermediate and Bottom Waters are relatively high in oxygen content from their recent contact with the surface, or with surface water, while the Deep Water is relatively low in oxygen content. The Deep Water can be divided into an Upper Deep of slightly higher temperature and salinity than the Lower Deep Water.

## ATLANTIC OCEAN

The *upper water circulation* of the Atlantic Ocean as a whole consists in its gross features of two great circulations or "gyres", a counter-clockwise one in the South Atlantic and a clockwise one in the North Atlantic (Fig. 19). At first sight it might seem appropriate to liken these two gyres to two gear wheels revolving and

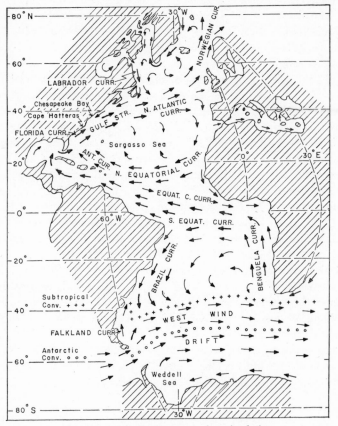

FIG. 19. *Atlantic Ocean—surface circulation.*

meshing near the equator. This, however, gives the impression that one may be driving the other, which is not the case. Rather the two gyres are driven separately, each by the trade winds in its own hemisphere, and they are separated over part of the equatorial region by an eastward flowing Counter Current.

In the South Atlantic the upper water gyre extends from the surface to a depth of about 200m near the equator and to about 800m at the southern limits of the gyre at the Subtropical Convergence. The different portions of this gyre have different water properties and have individual names which are given in Fig. 19. It is considered that the wind stress of the south-east trade winds between the equator and 10 to 15°S is the main driving force. This acts upon the sea and causes the South Equatorial Current to flow west toward the American side of the South Atlantic. Part of the current passes across the equator into the North Atlantic and will be discussed later. The remainder turns south along the South American continent as the Brazil Current. This turns east and continues across the Atlantic as part of the West Wind Drift and then turns north up the African side as the Benguela Current. The Brazil Current is warm and saline, having come from the trade wind region, while the Benguela Current is cold and less saline because of the contribution of Subantarctic water and of upwelling. A contribution to the water in the South Atlantic comes from the Falkland Current flowing north from Drake Passage up the coast of South America and separating the Brazil Current from this coast to about 25°S. The South Atlantic circulation is bounded on the south by the Subtropical Convergence. For simplicity the convergences are shown in Fig. 19 as lines but they must be considered in reality to be regions of convergence of finite extent and in some cases with seasonal variations in position. The Antarctic Convergence is fairly stable in position, not moving more than about $\pm 1$ degree of latitude, but the Subtropical Convergence may vary in position by several degrees of latitude.

In the North Atlantic, the clockwise gyre (Fig. 19) may be considered to start with the North Equatorial Current driven by the north-east trade winds. This current flows to the west and is joined from the south by that part of the South Equatorial Current which has turned across the equator into the North Atlantic. Part of this combined flow goes north-west as the Antilles Current outside the West Indies, and part goes between these islands and through the Caribbean and the Yucatan Channel into the Gulf of Mexico. In its passage through the Caribbean the flow is driven by the east winds of this region and the water piles up in the Gulf of Mexico. From here it escapes between Florida and Cuba into the North Atlantic as the Florida Current. The characteristics of this current indicate that its source is chiefly the North and South Equatorial Current water which traverses the Caribbean. Little of the water from the Gulf of Mexico itself appears to be carried out in this current. Off the coast of Florida the Florida Current is joined by the Antilles Current and from about Cape Hatteras where the combination breaks away from the North American shore it is called the Gulf Stream. The Florida Current water is distinguished by a salinity minimum due to Antarctic Intermediate Water brought in by the South Equatorial Current. The Antilles Current is composed mostly of North Atlantic Water and the salinity minimum is much less evident in it. The Gulf Stream flows north-east to the Grand Banks of Newfoundland at about 40°N and 50°W. From there, the flow which continues east and north is called the North Atlantic Current. This divides and part turns north-east between Scotland and Iceland and contributes to the circulation of the Norwegian, Greenland and Arctic Seas which will be described later. The remainder of the North Atlantic Current turns south past Spain and North Africa to complete the North Atlantic Gyre and to feed into the North Equatorial Current. The southward flow which covers the greater part of the North Atlantic as is shown in Fig. 19 is sometimes referred to as covering the Sargasso Sea. The currents are so slow and diffuse that it is hard to distinguish specific currents, although some authorities recognize a Canary Current flowing south off the coast of North Africa.

The salient feature of the North Atlantic Gyre is the fast,

concentrated flow of the Florida Current and the Gulf Stream on the west side contrasting with the broad, ill-defined southward flow just mentioned over the rest of the ocean. The Gulf Stream is sometimes misrepresented as an individual current of warm water distinct from its surroundings, like a "river in the ocean". It is better thought of as the rapidly moving edge of the Sargasso Sea, the 700 to 800 m deep pool of warm water which forms the upper layer of most of the North Atlantic Ocean. The Florida Current, which precedes the Gulf Stream, flows over the continental slope but the Gulf Stream itself is over deep water. The speeds of up to 250 cm/sec (5 knots) in the Gulf Stream are among the highest found in ocean currents. The Gulf Stream is usually sharply defined on its north-west side, but much less so on the south-east toward the centre of the gyre. Due to the small scale of Fig. 19 the Gulf Stream is shown as a series of straight arrows directed to the north-east. However, when examined in detail it can perhaps best be described as consisting of a series of filaments of current which are usually sinuous or meandering. While one can indicate on a chart the general region where these filaments which comprise the Gulf Stream are likely to be found, it is not possible to predict where they will be individually at any particular time. Some of these meanders were recorded in detail during an unusual oceanographic survey in 1950, called "Operation Cabot", when six oceanographic ships investigated a part of the Gulf Stream region simultaneously for three weeks. In particular, one meander developed to the extent that it broke off to form an individual eddy while the filament of current closed up behind it.

One feature of the circulation which was observed directly for the first time in 1957 was that underneath the north-eastward flowing Gulf Stream was a south to south-westward flowing counter current with speeds of 9 to 18 cm/sec. Earlier studies by the methods of dynamical oceanography had suggested the possibility of such a current but the different interpretations were not consistent and to many oceanographers the idea of a significant current close to the bottom was not acceptable. However, Stommel had developed a theory of the thermohaline circulation from which there was good reason to expect such a southward deep current. The 1957 measurements made with Swallow floats demonstrated that in the region of about 33°N, 75°W it certainly did exist at that time. Wüst has computed that a similar southward current must occur in the western South Atlantic, and Japanese measurements in 1960 suggest the existence of a southward flow below the Kuroshio on the west side of the Pacific. At the same time it must be stated that later Swallow float measurements in the Atlantic have indicated that the counter current may not always be present under the Gulf Stream. Also, measurements off Bermuda in a region where strong currents were not expected showed currents at 2000 m averaging 6 cm/sec with a maximum of 20 cm/sec and at 4000 m averaging 12 cm/sec with a maximum of 42 cm/sec. In the eastern North Atlantic off Portugal, measurements at 1500 to 4000 m indicated currents of 1 to 2 cm/sec. with maxima of 5 cm/sec. Small currents were expected and found here but the general trend of direction was south-east rather than north as would have been expected from Stommel's thermohaline circulation theory. These later observations raise some doubt as to the significance of the earlier measurements of the Gulf Stream counter current, and emphasize our lack of understanding in general of deep ocean currents. One thing, however, is clear. The old notion that deep currents are slow and steady must be abandoned—they appear to be just as variable as surface currents and can have quite respectable speeds.

Figure 20 shows the distribution of temperature and salinity in a cross-section across the Gulf Stream. The Stream itself is associated for dynamic reasons with the steeply sloping isotherms and isohalines in a relatively narrow band of about 120 km width shown. The fact that the water to the left of the current is cold compared to that at the same depth on the right, and the steepness of the isotherms in such a section, gave rise to the term "cold wall" to describe the water to the left of the Stream. Although the term is striking, it must be remembered that the real slope of the isotherms in the sea here is only of the order of 1 in 200. This is certainly steep for the

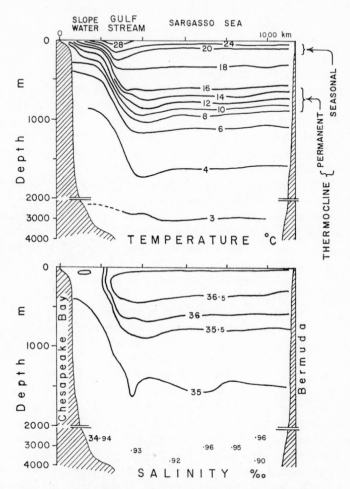

FIG. 20.   *Temperature and salinity sections across the Gulf Stream, August/September, 1932 (according to Iselin).*

slope of a surface in the sea but it is not much for a wall! It is clear from the sections that the Gulf Stream is not an individual flow of warm water and is hardly distinguished from the Sargasso Sea water to its right. One other feature is the wide spacing between the 16° and the 20° isotherms over most of the section. A body of so-called "18° water" is a permanent feature of the west side of the Sargasso Sea (since it was first observed by the *Challenger* in 1873) and its properties are very consistent within a few tenths of a degree on either side of 18°C and with a salinity of 36·4 to 36·6‰. If it is winter formed water the remarkable feature is the consistency of its properties, particularly temperature considering the variation of air temperatures in winter.

The volume transport of the Florida Current averages about 26 sv but measurements by the electromagnetic method (Chapter 6) have shown variations from 15 to 38 sv. For the Gulf Stream proper the total north-eastward transport across a section from Chesapeake Bay has been estimated as from 74 to 93 sv. This includes the water of the Florida Current plus the Antilles Current of about 12 sv, and a considerable volume of water which circulates in the inner part of the North Atlantic Gyre.

For a complete and stimulating account of the Gulf Stream, including the history of its study, the observations available, and the theories for its structure, the reader is referred to *The Gulf Stream* by Henry Stommel.

Between the Gulf Stream and the shore of North America there is a south-westward flowing coastal current with an elongated counter clockwise eddy between it and the Stream. The exact mechanism which maintains this eddy has been much discussed as a problem in dynamical oceanography. The coastal current is partly supplied from the Labrador Current which flows south out of the Labrador Sea between Labrador and the southern tip of Greenland. The presence of this southward-flowing, cold, low-salinity Labrador water in proximity to the warm, saline waters of the Gulf Stream gives rise to a very complicated oceanographic situation in this western part of the North Atlantic.

The North Atlantic Current is sometimes described as consisting of several branches or filaments of current forming a continuation from the Gulf Stream. Fuglister has taken data for the region between 75°W and 52°W for several cruises within a short period of time in 1953 and shown three significantly different interpretations of the same data. These interpretations vary from a single rather tortuous stream to a large number of fairly straight filaments. This exercise demonstrates the deficiencies in our observational knowledge of this region. The density of observations which it is practical to make is still low and the observations are not sufficiently simultaneous to give an adequate picture.

In the Equatorial Atlantic, between the westward flowing North and South Equatorial Currents, there is an eastward flowing Equatorial Counter Current, which is most evident in the eastern side of the equatorial region. The equatorial current system is more clearly developed in the Pacific than in the Atlantic and this typical feature of the ocean circulation will be described in more detail in the section on the Pacific Ocean.

When studying the *water mass characteristics* of the Atlantic Ocean we are fortunate in having a considerable amount of information and in particular the data from two extensive expeditions, both of which covered the greater part of the area systematically and in a relatively short time. The two expeditions were the German *Meteor* expedition during 1925 to 1927, and the International Geophysical Year studies of 1957 to 1958 carried out by the Woods Hole Oceanographic Institution of the United States with co-operation from the National Institute of Oceanography of Great Britain. The second of these studies was deliberately arranged to cover the South and Equatorial Atlantic along the same lines of stations as those occupied by the *Meteor* in order to obtain a direct comparison of the distribution of water properties after the interval of about thirty years. One of the immediate results of the comparison of the two sets of data was the recognition that the distributions of temperature, salinity and dissolved oxygen were almost identical. This result was very comforting to oceanographers who have made a practice of assuming that the state of affairs which they observe in the ocean is a reasonably steady one, at least when averaged over a year to eliminate seasonal changes.

The opportunity will be taken here to explain that a "steady state" does not necessarily imply that everything is motionless. In the steady state, some or all parts of the system may be moving but at no point is there any change of motion with time.

In the surface layer in the Atlantic, the salient temperature characteristic is that it is high at low latitudes and lower at high latitudes (Figs. 6 and 7). Between the equator and about 20°N the temperature ranges between 25° and 28°C with little seasonal change. In the South Atlantic, south of the equator to 40°S, there is a seasonal change of temperature of about 5C° between winter and summer; at higher latitudes the seasonal range of temperature decreases. In the North Atlantic the difference between winter and summer temperatures rises to 10C° at 40°N and then decreases at high latitudes. The salinity does not show any significant seasonal change (except close to ice). There is a minimum value of 35‰ just north of the equator and then maxima of 37·3‰ in the tropics at about 20°N and S. From here the salinity decreases to 34‰ or less at high latitudes.

There is a marked difference in the surface water characteristics between the west (American) and east (European-African) sides. In the North Atlantic there is a difference of about 25C° in the sea surface temperature between Florida and Labrador, compared to only about 10C° between the same latitudes on the east side (North Africa to Scotland). In salinity there is a south–north difference of about 3‰ on the west compared to 1·5‰ on the east. These differences between west and east are clearly associated with the differences in currents. In the west, the Gulf Stream carries a concentrated flow of warm, saline water to the north-east along the continent whereas in the east the southward flow is slow and diffuse. The southward flowing Labrador Current carries cold, low salinity water to the south along the Canadian coast and the combination of this southward cold current with the northward warm current of the Gulf Stream is the cause of the large temperature differential along this coast.

In the South Atlantic, the effect of the Brazil Current is present but is much less conspicuous than that of the Gulf Stream. The Falkland Current flowing up the coast of South America is evident in low temperatures and salinities along the coast to nearly 25° S. On the east side, low temperatures immediately off the coast of South Africa are due to upwelling of subsurface water. Low salinities in this region are also characteristic of this water, but the low salinities farther north off equatorial Africa are due to river runoff.

The average $[TS]$ characteristics of the waters below the surface layer are shown in Fig. 21a. The upper waters below the surface layer appear on this diagram as the Atlantic Central Waters extending to depths of 300 m on either side of the equator and deepening to 600 to 900 m at mid-latitudes and then getting somewhat shallower at high latitudes. Both of the Central Water masses appear on the $[TS]$ diagram as straight lines extending from high temperature and salinity to lower temperature and salinity. The lines indicate the mean values; the individual points extend over a range of about $\pm 0.1\%_0$ of the mean. At first sight, the Central Water Masses might appear to be examples of water masses produced by the vertical mixing of water types represented by the characteristics at the ends of the bands. This however is believed not to be the case. Iselin has suggested that these water masses originate by sinking equatorward of the subtropical convergences. The cooler, less saline water sinks at higher latitudes and flows equatorward while the warmer, more saline water sinks at lower latitudes and flows equatorward above the cooler water. If one examines the winter $[TS]$ characteristics in the north–south horizontal direction at the surface over a range of latitudes near the subtropical convergences one finds the same $[TS]$ characteristics as one finds in the vertical below the surface in the Central Water masses at lower latitudes. In the South Atlantic the Central Water terminates at depth where it merges into the well defined Antarctic Intermediate Water. In the North Atlantic the Arctic Intermediate Water is a much less

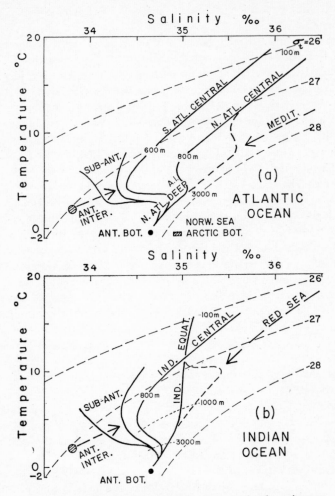

FIG. 21.  *Average temperature/salinity diagrams for the main water masses of the Atlantic and the Indian Oceans. (Adapted by permission from Sverdrup, Johnson and Fleming,* The Oceans, their Physics, Chemistry and General Biology, *(C) 1942 by Prentice-Hall Inc., Englewood Cliffs, N.J.)*

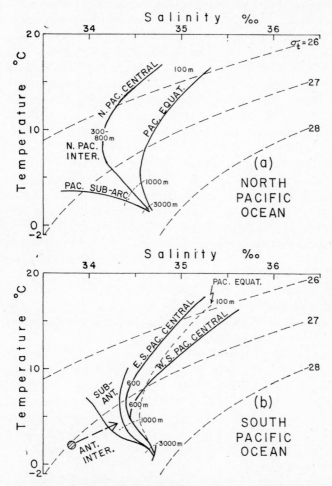

FIG. 22.  *Average temperature/salinity diagrams for the main water masses of the Pacific Ocean. (Adapted by permission from Sverdrup, Johnson and Fleming, The Oceans, their Physics, Chemistry and General Biology, (C) 1942 by Prentice-Hall Inc., Englewood Cliffs, N.J.)*

significant water body and the Central Water merges into this at high latitudes and into the Mediterranean Water at lower latitudes.

The main features of the *deep water characteristics* and *circulation* of the Atlantic are well shown in Fig. 23 which is based upon Wüst's description from the *Meteor* data. The three sections in the figure show the temperature, salinity and oxygen distributions from south to north along the western trough of the Atlantic Ocean, i.e. between the American continents and the mid-Atlantic Ridge.

The temperature section shows clearly that the largest variations both horizontally and vertically are in the upper layer, and emphasizes the statement made earlier that the vertical property gradients in the sea are generally much greater than the horizontal ones.

South of about 60° S there is the relatively homogeneous Antarctic Circumpolar Water with a temperature close to 0°C and a salinity of 34·6‰. The Antarctic Intermediate Water which sinks at the Antarctic Convergence is evident to some extent as a low temperature tongue centred at 1000 m, but is much clearer as a low salinity tongue extending to 25° N. It is also apparent, although less clearly, by an oxygen maximum at about 800 m depth to the equator. Below this and flowing along the bottom to the north is the cold Antarctic Bottom Water which can be traced by its temperature, salinity and high oxygen content to about 40° N.

Between the Intermediate Water above and the Bottom Water below there is the great bulk of the Deep Water which is most evident on the salinity and oxygen sections. It originates at the surface in the vicinity of 60° N, being formed by winter cooling of the relatively saline North Atlantic surface water. This sinks and then flows south between 1500 and 4000 m depth, having a relatively small range of properties, 2·2° to 3·5°C and 34·90 to 34·97‰.

The evidence that the Deep Water is formed in the North Atlantic comes from tracing the water characteristics back to the surface in this region. Nansen in 1912 suggested that the water is formed in the winter at the surface and then sinks by convection. Recently Dietrich has presented data obtained by German

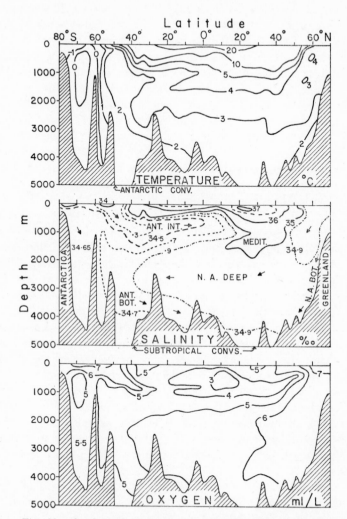

FIG. 23.   *South–north longitudinal sections of water characteristics along the western trough of the Atlantic Ocean (after Wüst).*

oceanographers in 1958, during the International Geophysical Year, which show clearly what happens. In the region south of the southern tip of Greenland the water properties in late winter were almost uniform from the surface to near the bottom. For instance the temperatures from surface to 3000 m ranged only between 3° and 3·25°C in an area over 150 km across. From this column, a tongue of 3° to 3·25°C water extended south at depths of 2000 to 2500 m. This water also had a high oxygen content; even at 2000 m depth it was still 90% of that at the surface. The explanation for these observations is that the deep water was actually forming at the time, being cooled at the surface and sinking rapidly to 2000 to 3000 m depth, and then continuing south at its density level as North Atlantic Deep Water.

The vertical convective sinking does not carry the Deep Water quite to the bottom. Evidence is growing for the existence of a North Atlantic or Sub-Polar Bottom Water, although it has only a small volume compared to the Antarctic Bottom Water. The evidence is that this cold water, of temperature 1°C or less, is found against the lower part of the continental slope off eastern Greenland and the property distributions suggest that it is flowing south into the Western Atlantic Trough. It is presumed to come over the Greenland–Iceland ridge from the north. There is also evidence that cold, dense water from the Norwegian Sea flows intermittently to the south over the ridge between Iceland and the Faroes into the Eastern Atlantic Trough. An intensive programme of study of this flow (the "Overflow Programme") was started in 1959, arrangements being made to have several oceanographic vessels working in the area at the same time in order to obtain simultaneous data on the water-property distributions and on currents.

The bottom waters in the western and eastern basins of the Atlantic have noticeably different properties in the South Atlantic because of the barrier of the mid-Atlantic Ridge. Figure 24a shows transverse sections of temperature and salinity across the ocean at 16°S to illustrate this. On the west side the Antarctic Bottom

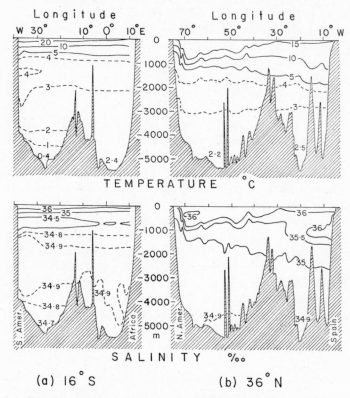

FIG. 24.  *West–east sections of temperature and salinity across the Atlantic Ocean at 16° S and 36° N (after Fuglister,* Atlantic Ocean Atlas, *Vol. I, Woods Hole Oceanographic Institution).*

Water has temperatures down to 0·4°C whereas in the east side the minimum is 2·4°C. The Antarctic Bottom Water is kept out of the eastern basin by the Walfish Ridge with a sill depth of less than 3500 m extending from Africa to the mid-Atlantic Ridge.  The salinity difference between the two sides is less remarkable, 34·7‰ on the west compared to 34·9‰ on the east.  It is interesting to note that the densities on either side of the Ridge are identical, the temperature and salinity differences being in such directions as to cancel in their effect on density. Other water masses evident in this figure are the Antarctic Intermediate with its low salinity core at about 800 m and the more saline North Atlantic Deep Water with its higher salinity core at about 2500 m.

Further north at 36°N (Fig. 24b) the temperature difference has fallen to only 0·3C° and the salinities are almost identical. The influence of the outflow of Mediterranean Water is evident with its core at about 1000 m in the salinity section, but less evident in the temperature section because the water has settled at a level determined by its density which is determined mainly by temperature. At the west the steep slopes of the isotherms and isohalines associated with the Gulf Stream are also evident in the upper water.

By careful analysis using the core method the Mediterranean water can be traced down through the South Atlantic. The effect of the Mediterranean Water can be seen in the [TS] diagram (Fig. 21a) as a salinity maximum above the Deep Water maximum. The Mediterranean maximum is very marked for waters of the eastern North Atlantic but is less conspicuous in the west and in the south as it gradually loses its characteristic properties by mixing with the waters above and below it.

Wüst has made calculations of the *volume transport* of water in the South Atlantic and these are interesting both as descriptive of that ocean and as examples of the application of oceanographic principles. When considering Wüst's calculations it must be remembered that there were no direct current measurements of any consequence available to him, and the volume transports had to be deduced indirectly. Calculation by the geostrophic equation (see *Dynamical Oceanography*) from the density distribution gave the relative currents from top to bottom across the ocean. To make the relative currents absolute a depth of no motion was chosen between the Antarctic Intermediate Water which must flow north and the Deep Water which must flow south. This depth varies over the ocean but is at about 1400 m for a section at 30°S from the South American to the African shore. These absolute currents then could be used to determine the flow at various depths and positions across the section.    The resulting volume transports had to satisfy the condition of continuity of volume, i.e. there must be no net flow to the north or to the south through the trans-oceanic section. This condition is based on the observation that mean sea-level north or south of the section is not changing significantly.    It also assumes that there is no net flow into or out of the North Atlantic + Arctic Sea combination.    (There are certainly large exchanges of water between the Atlantic and the Arctic but these are internal in the present discussion and cannot affect the mean sea-level).    The assumption of no net flow into the Atlantic + Arctic combination is not quite true because there is some flow through the Bering Strait from the Pacific into the Arctic. Sverdrup estimated this at about 0·3 sv on the average.    More recent estimates and measurements suggest that it may be greater than this, up to about 1 sv, but even this is small compared to the volume transports through the section at 30° S across the South Atlantic.    Conservation of salt in the North and South Atlantic Oceans also had to be satisfied.

Sverdrup summarized the volume transports calculated by Wüst as follows.    In the upper layer there is a transport to the north of about 23 sv on the east side (Benguela Current and South Atlantic Gyre) as against 17 sv to the south on the west side (Brazil Current and the Gyre).    The Antarctic Intermediate Water has a transport of 9 sv to the north, the Deep Water has a transport of 18 sv to the south, and the Bottom Water has a transport of 3 sv to the north. There is therefore a net transport to the north of 18 sv in the upper layers (from the surface to 1400 m depth) together with the bottom Water, balanced by 18 sv to the south in the Deep Water.    This represents a fairly rapid rate of exchange of water in the north-south direction in the South Atlantic Ocean.

## MEDITERRANEAN, BLACK AND BALTIC SEAS

The *Mediterranean Sea* is of interest in displaying some results of the interaction between the atmosphere and the sea. Due to the heat input and the large excess of evaporation over precipitation the water in this region is characterized by high temperatures and salinities which are surpassed only in the Red Sea.

The Mediterranean is divided essentially into a western and an eastern basin by a sill of depth about 400 m extending from Sicily to the north African coast. The maximum depths are about 3400 m in the western basin and 4200 m in the eastern.

The two characteristic Mediterranean water masses are the Intermediate Water and the Deep Water. The former, called by Wüst the Levantine Intermediate Water, is formed in the winter off the south coast of Turkey with a temperature of 15°C and a salinity of 39·1‰. It flows west at 200 to 600 m depth, along the North African coast and out below the surface through the Strait of Gibraltar into the Atlantic. By the time it starts to flow down the continental slope its properties have been modified to 13°C and 37·3‰ by mixing during its passage from the east and particularly through the Strait. The outflow below the surface is replaced by a surface inflow from the Atlantic. It should be noted that the water which emerges from the Mediterranean is this Intermediate Water and not water which has spilled or been displaced out of the deeper basins.

The Deep and Bottom Waters are formed at the northern edges of the basins in winter, chiefly off the Riviera in the western basin and in the southern Adriatic Sea in the eastern basin. In the western basin the deep water potential temperature is 12·6°C and the salinity 38·4‰, in the eastern basin the properties are 13·2°C and 38·65‰ with very high $\sigma_t$ values of up to 29·2. These values may be contrasted with those at 4000 m in the Atlantic of 2·4°C, 34·9‰ and a $\sigma_t$ of 27·8. The oxygen content of the water in these basins is fairly high, up to 4·7 ml/l in the western and 5·0 ml/l in the eastern, suggesting frequent replenishment by the considerable vertical convection which carries the winter formed water down to the depths of the basins.

The oceanographic characteristics of the *Black Sea* which connects with the eastern Mediterranean are in direct contrast to those described above. The Black Sea has a maximum depth of 2240 m and connects with the Mediterranean through the narrow passages of the Bosphorus and the Dardanelles, which have depths of only 40 to 100 m. The Deep Water in the Black Sea has a salinity of only 22·3‰ and a potential temperature of 8·8°C. There is no dissolved oxygen below about 180 m. It is replaced by hydrogen sulphide whose concentration increases with depth.

There is evidence that in geological time the water in the Black Sea has varied from being fresh to moderately saline and it is not known whether the present deep water salinity represents a steady state or not. There is a considerable river runoff of fresh water into the Sea and, at most, a very limited influx of salt water from the Mediterranean. The currents through the Bosphorus and the Dardanelles consist of a surface outflow of low salinity water, carrying the precipitation and river runoff, and a subsurface inflow of more saline water. The narrowness and shallowness of the passage results in considerable current speeds and current shear, and the consequent turbulence causes vertical mixing. The result is that the surface water which leaves the Black Sea with a salinity of about 16‰ reaches the Mediterranean with a salinity increased to 30‰, while the incoming subsurface water leaves the Mediterranean with a salinity of 38·5‰ which is reduced to 35 to 30‰ by the time it reaches the Black Sea. There is some difference of opinion among those who have studied the flow through these passages as to how much saline water actually flows into the Black Sea. There is no doubt that there is a considerable flow from the Mediterranean into the Dardanelles but much of this saline water is mixed upward and carried out in the surface layer and so does not reach the Black Sea. This is an example of the estuarine type of circulation which will be discussed later. It is evident from the stagnant condition of the deep water of the Black Sea that the amount of saline water which penetrates through the Bosphorus and sinks in the Sea must be small and insufficient to refresh the deep layers. Even at the maximum rate of inflow measured where the saline Mediterranean water enters the Dardanelles it is calculated that it would take some 2500 years for a volume equal to that of the Black Sea to pass in. This contrasts with the situation in the Mediterranean where the inflow through the Strait of Gibraltar is such that it would take only about 75 years for a volume equal to that of the Mediterranean to flow in.

The *Baltic Sea*, including the Gulf of Bothnia and the Gulf of Finland, shows some features which may be compared with those of the Mediterranean and Black Seas. In contrast to the Mediterranean the Baltic is shallow, with an average depth of only 100 m and a maximum of 460 m. Like the Black Sea it has an excess of precipitation and river runoff over evaporation. In consequence the salinity is low, usually below 10‰ at the surface and rising only to 12 to 16‰ at 5°C in the deep water. The Baltic, however, does not exhibit permanent stagnation, possibly because of the moderate depths. The communication with the North Sea outside is through shallow passages with a sill depth of 18 m and much mixing occurs between the outflowing surface layer and the inflowing more saline one. As a result of this the average inflow of saline water into the Baltic is small. However, tides play a significant part in assisting the introduction of saline water. In addition the stress due to the wind is sometimes sufficient to override the two layer flow and cause unidirectional flow at all depths through the entrance passages. Neither of these processes plays any significant part in the flow into the Black Sea.

## NORTHERN ADJACENT SEAS

Bordering the North Atlantic are two adjacent areas of some significance, the Norwegian and Greenland Seas to the east of Greenland and the Labrador Sea and Baffin Bay area to the west

(Fig. 25). The Norwegian Current is a continuation of part of the North Atlantic Current which turns north and passes over the Wyville–Thompson Ridge between the Shetland and Faroe Islands into the *Norwegian* and *Greenland Seas*. Along the Greenland coast there is the south-westward flowing East Greenland Current which is composed of the outflow from the Arctic and some water from the Norwegian Current. The speeds in these two currents are up to 30 cm/sec. They are upper layer currents and the submarine ridges which extend from Greenland to Scotland with maximum depths of less than 1000 m prevent deeper Atlantic water from entering the Norwegian Sea and hence the Arctic. Between the two currents are gyral circulations in the Norwegian and Greenland Seas.

A rather curious feature is that apparently the subsurface water which enters the Arctic Sea from this area comes from the gyre of the Norwegian Sea to the south rather than from the Greenland Sea which is north of it and closer to the Arctic. This was shown by Metcalf from data obtained in the winters of 1951 to 1955. Characteristically, the water of the Greenland Gyre above 1500 m has properties of $-1 \cdot 1$ to $-1 \cdot 7°C$ and $34 \cdot 86$ to $34 \cdot 90\%_0$, while below this depth the water is almost isohaline at $34 \cdot 92\%_0$ with a temperature of $-1 \cdot 1°C$ or colder. The deep water of the Norwegian Gyre has the same salinity but its temperature is $-0 \cdot 95°C$ or warmer, properties which are similar to those of the Bottom Water of the Arctic basin. This Norwegian Sea water is also found to the east and north of the Greenland Sea and apparently in some way forms a barrier to the passage of the colder Greenland Gyre water into the Arctic.

The deep waters of both the Norwegian and Greenland Seas have high oxygen contents of 6 to 7·5 ml/l indicating frequent formation, presumably by winter cooling at the surface. In addition, evidence has been accumulating recently to indicate that some of the deep water passes southward over the ridge east of Iceland into the Atlantic. It is possible that this flow is sporadic and in the oceanographic "Overflow Programme" this area will be studied in detail both in space and in time with respect to the inflow from the Atlantic in the upper layers and to the deep outflow.

The East Greenland Current carries much ice from the Arctic down the coast of Greenland, maintaining the low temperatures and rendering access to the east coast of Greenland difficult. The Current flows round the southern tip of Greenland into the *Labrador Sea*, having picked up some Atlantic water south-west of Iceland. It continues north up the west coast as the West Greenland Current from which water branches off to the west until the Current eventually peters out in *Baffin Bay*. The inflow to this area is balanced by the southward flow, along the west side of Baffin Bay, of the Baffin Land Current which continues as the Labrador Current down the west side of the Labrador Sea back into the Atlantic. In this region the difference between the properties of the in- and outflowing currents is not as great as to the east of Greenland. The West Greenland Current has temperatures around 2°C and salinities of 31 to 34‰, while the Labrador Current water is at 0°C or less and 30 to 34‰. The frequently quoted calculations of Smith, Soule and Mosby indicate that above 1500m depth the inflow of the East Greenland Current carries about 7·5sv while the outflow of the Labrador Current amounts to about 5·6sv. They conclude that the balance of 1·9sv must flow out as deep water from the Labrador Sea into the Atlantic. Other estimates have indicated that considerable variations in the net flow may occur but the concensus is that in the long term average there is a net inflow in the upper layers and an outflow of deep water.

The circulation of the Labrador Sea–Baffin Bay region then combines some of the features of the Norwegian Sea and of the European Mediterranean. There are the horizontally separated in- and outflows together with a deep outflow. The latter is formed by sinking when the density of the surface water is increased by winter cooling, without freezing, of moderately saline Atlantic water in the Labrador Sea south-west of Greenland. This vertical convection is the reason for the small range of water properties in the Labrador Sea, from 2 to 3·5°C and 34·9 to 35·0‰ with the relatively high oxygen content of 6 to 6·5 ml/l over a depth range of 3000 m. This water contributes to the North Atlantic Deep Water.

The Labrador Sea is open to the Atlantic to depths of over 4000 m but Baffin Bay, with a maximum depth of 2200 m, is separated from the Labrador Sea and hence from the Atlantic, by the sill in the Davis Strait of depth only about 600 m. The deep waters in Baffin Bay below sill depth are markedly different from those at the same depths outside. The temperature is between 0° and −0·5°C and the salinity 34·5‰ with relatively low oxygen values of 4 ml/l. Sverdrup interpreted the Baffin Deep Water as Labrador Sea water which had moved north below the surface, mixed with cool, low salinity surface water, and then had its density sufficiently increased by freezing to sink to fill the basin. Since Baffin Bay is ice-covered during the winter there is little information for this season but there are indications that water having the properties of the Deep Baffin Water does not occur at the surface. An alternative suggestion by Bailey is that the source of the Baffin Deep Water is probably inflow from the Arctic through the passage between Greenland and Ellesmere Island. Water of the same temperature and salinity as the Baffin Deep Water certainly occurs at the appropriate depth in the Arctic Sea. The annual inflow to Baffin Bay is presumably relatively small so that the water in the basin has a long residence time there and the oxygen content gets depleted.

Some contribution to the Labrador Current comes from Hudson Bay. This is an extensive body of water though relatively shallow, averaging only about 90 m in depth. There is considerable seasonal river runoff into the Bay giving rise to a marked horizontal stratification determined by the salinity. The upper water properties vary from 23‰ at up to 10°C in the summer to 30‰ at −1·6°C in the winter. The deeper water has a temperature of −1·0 to −1·8°C at salinities of 32 to 33·5‰ in different locations, with little seasonal variation as far as is known. This summary of water properties of Hudson Bay is based on Hachey's investigations of 1930. Recent Canadian observations from 1961 on are expected to provide a much more detailed picture for the summer. The considerable river runoff into Hudson Bay remains largely in the upper layer which has a counter-clockwise circulation and discharges through Hudson Strait to add to the Labrador Current.

Sverdrup contrasted the horizontally separated inflow and outflow of these northern seas with the vertically separated flows into and out of the Mediterranean. In each case the outflowing water is considerably modified with respect to the inflowing water but in opposite senses. The water of the North Atlantic Current which becomes the Norwegian Current has temperatures from 4° to 13°C and salinities from 34·9 to 35·3‰, whereas the outflowing East Greenland Current water is at −1·5 to 2°C and 31 to 34‰. On a [TS] diagram the upper waters of the Norwegian Current are represented by a line roughly parallel to the temperature axis, with the density mainly determined by temperature, whereas the upper layer water of the East Greenland Current is represented by a line roughly parallel to the salinity axis with the density determined almost entirely by salinity as is characteristic of high latitude conditions.

## ARCTIC SEA

Our knowledge of the Arctic Sea has developed considerably since the mid-1950's. Numerous soundings and oceanographic stations have been taken from ships, as well as through the ice from semi-permanent camps on ice islands or ice floes or from temporary camps established by aircraft transportation. In particular it has been demonstrated that the Arctic Sea is divided into two basins by the Lomonosov Ridge which extends from Greenland past the North Pole to Siberia (Fig. 25). These two basins have been named by LaFond the Canadian Basin (depth about 3800m) and the Eurasian Basin (depth about 4200m). Soundings along the Lomonosov Ridge are not numerous enough to determine its sill depth with any certainty but comparisons of water properties

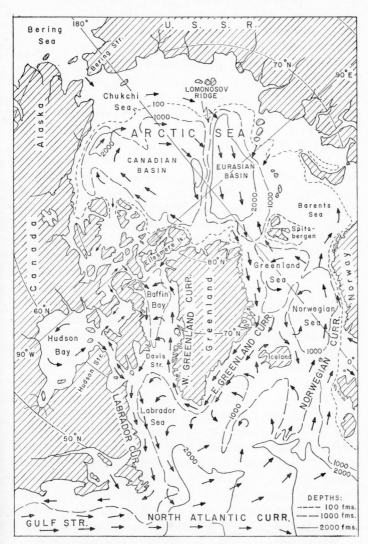

FIG. 25.  *Arctic Sea and North Atlantic adjacent seas, bathymetry and surface currents.*

on either side suggest that it is at 1200 to 1400m below sea-level. A feature of the bottom topography is the broad continental shelf off Siberia, 200 to 800km wide and occupying about 36% of the area of the Arctic Sea but containing only 2% of the total volume of water in that sea. The main connection with the other oceans is with the Atlantic through the gap between Greenland and Spitzbergen with a main sill depth of 1500m. A narrow channel with depths to 3000m reported by Soviet oceanographers does not appear to pass any significant amount of water into the Arctic. The Bering Strait connection to the Bering Sea and the Pacific has a sill depth of 50m and is narrow, but the water flow into the Arctic is significant. There are also connections from the Arctic through the Canadian Archipelago by several channels which lead to Baffin Bay and Davis Strait and thence to the Atlantic. The northern passages are difficult of access because of ice and are not fully charted.

Information on the *circulation in the upper layers* has been obtained from the records of the movements of ships held in the ice, such as the *Fram* and the *Sedov*, and from the movements of camps on the ice. In addition, geostrophic calculations have been made from the water density distribution. These various sources yield a consistent picture of the surface layer movement which is best described as a clockwise circulation in the Canadian Basin leading out to the East Greenland Current, and, in the Eurasian Basin, a movement by the most direct path toward Greenland and out in the East Greenland Current. The speeds are of the order of 1 to 4 cm/sec. These speeds are better stated as 300 to 1200 km/year when one is considering them in relation to the size of the Arctic Sea which is approximately 4000 km across. The speed and distance may be compared with the 3 years taken by the *Fram* to drift from north of the Bering Strait to Spitzbergen, and the $2\frac{1}{2}$ years for the *Sedov* to drift about 3000 km. The movement is not by any means steady but has frequent variations in speed and direction which average out to the figures quoted.

Coachman, in 1962, completed a new description of the *water masses of the Arctic.* Three main water masses are recognized, the surface or Arctic Water from the sea surface to 200 m depth, the Atlantic Water from 200 to 900 m, and the Bottom Water from 900 m to the bottom. One of the features of the water structure is that the density is largely determined by the salinity.

The Arctic Water (0 to 200 m) can be divided into three layers which will be called the surface, the subsurface and the lower layers.

The surface layer is much the same across the whole Arctic and extends from the surface to 25 to 50 m depth. The salinity is strongly influenced by the melting or freezing of ice and has a wide range from 28 to 33·5‰. The temperature also is controlled by the melting or freezing of ice which involves considerable heat transfer at constant temperature (the freezing point). In consequence the temperature remains close to the freezing point of the water which varies only from −1·5°C at a salinity at 28‰ to −1·8°C at a salinity of 33·5‰. Seasonal variations in water properties are limited to this layer and range up to 2‰ in salinity and 0·2C° in temperature.

The subsurface layer (25/50 m to 100 m) in the Eurasian Basin is isothermal to 100 m (Fig. 26b) but there is a strong halocline between 25 and 100 m (Fig. 26a). Below 100 m the temperature increases markedly but the salinity only increases slowly. The fact that the subsurface water is isothermal but not isohaline indicates that its structure cannot be due to vertical mixing between the surface layer and the deeper layers. It is probable that the subsurface water is maintained by horizontal advection (flow) from the Eurasian shelf. The mechanism suggested by Coachman is that the saline Atlantic Water which enters near Spitzbergen continues below the surface along the Eurasian continental slope which is indented by several deep submarine canyons. At the same time the considerable river runoff from northern Asia flows north as a cold, low-salinity surface layer over the shelf. It mixes at its subsurface contact with the warmer, more saline Atlantic Water to form the subsurface water which is close to its freezing point. The subsurface water continues out into the Arctic Sea to maintain the layer there between 25m and 100m. The canyons are necessary to feed the saline Atlantic Water into the shelf area, and the vertical mixing process is similar to that which occurs in an estuary where fresh river water flows over saline sea-water as described later.

The subsurface water in the Canadian Basin also shows a halocline from 25m to 100m but its temperature structure is different from that in the Eurasian Basin. There is a characteristic temperature maximum at 75 to 100m depth (Fig. 26c) with a consequent

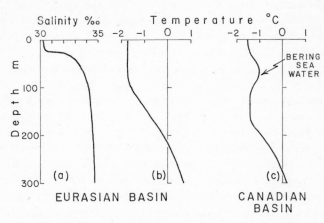

FIG. 26. *Salinity and temperature profiles for the Arctic Water Mass (after Coachman).*

temperature minimum of −1·5°C at about 150m and then an increase to the deeper water. The temperature maximum is attributed to Bering Sea water coming into the Arctic through the Bering Strait. This water is warmer than the Arctic surface layer but slightly denser because of its salinity. It presents one of the few examples of a subsurface temperature maximum occuring in the ocean. The reason that it occurs here is because the water is close to its freezing point and the effect of salinity preponderates over that of temperature in determining density. The temperature maximum is found to be most prominent in the Chukchi Sea north of the Bering Strait, and it diminishes around the clockwise circulation of the Canadian Basin.

The lower layer of the Arctic Water is essentially a mixing layer between the subsurface Arctic Water above and the Atlantic Water below.

The second water mass, the Atlantic Water, is recognized chiefly by having a higher temperature than the water above or below it. Where it enters, on the Spitzbergen side of the Greenland–Spitzbergen gap, its temperature is up to 3°C and its salinity 34·8 to 35·1‰. In the Arctic Sea its temperature decreases gradually to 0·4°C and its salinity is within the limited range from 34·85 to 35·0‰. Its movement has been traced by the "core" method along the Eurasian continental slope, with some water branching off to the north and out in the East Greenland Current. The remainder flows across the Lomonosov Ridge into the Canadian Basin. The water mass itself appears to remain in the depth range from 200 to 900m, but the depth of the temperature maximum increases from 150m near Spitzbergen to nearly 500m in the Canadian Basin. The reason is that the temperature gradient in the upward direction is greater than in the downward one. The result is that more heat is lost upward from the layer than downward and the temperature maximum increases in depth without the water descending. The circulation of this Atlantic Water is basically counter-clockwise round the Arctic Sea, the opposite direction to the movement of the Arctic Water above it.

The Arctic Bottom Water extends from about 900m depth to the bottom and comprises about 60% of the total water volume of the Arctic Sea. Its salinity range through the whole volume is very small, from 34·90 to 34·99‰, and in any particular area the change in the vertical direction is generally smaller than this. There is a tendency, if anything, for the salinity to increase very slightly with depth. The in situ temperature varies over a range of 0·2C° in the vertical column. In the Eurasian Basin the temperature reaches a minimum of −0·8°C at 2500m, while in the Canadian Basin the minimum is −0·4°C at 2000m. Below the minimum the temperature rises by about 0·2C° to the bottom. The rate of increase is equal to the adiabatic rate, i.e. it can be attributed entirely to the compression of the water as it sinks. It is believed that this Bottom Water originates in the Norwegian Sea and flows thence into the Arctic. The reason for the higher temperature of the water in the Canadian Basin than in the Eurasian is that the former is water which has come across the Lomonosov Ridge at depths not greater than 1200 to 1400m. The deeper, colder water which gets into the Eurasian Basin is prevented from entering the Canadian Basin by the Lomonosov Ridge.

The Arctic Sea has always attracted het attention of oceanographers wishing to exercise their talents by investigating the *water budget*, and many sets of calculations have been made. The results obtained vary somewhat in detail but the main features are substantially the same. Recent calculations suggest the following approximate figures for the in- and outflows:

TABLE 4

*Water Budget of the Arctic Ocean (average values)*

| IN | | OUT | |
|---|---|---|---|
| From Atlantic | 3·5 sv | East Greenland Current | 3·7 sv |
| From Pacific | 1 sv | Through Canadian Archipelago | 0·9 sv |
| From rivers and precipitation | 0·1 sv | | |

Calculations of water budgets are done for other reasons than for displaying virtuosity in calculation and deduction. From the water budget, in relation to the volume of the basin itself, one can obtain an idea of the rate at which the water in the basin is exchanged. This may be important for determining the rate of replenishment of nutrients in an area important for fisheries or for the rate of removal of sewage or industrial effluent. For the Arctic it is estimated that the surface water is substantially all replaced in a period of 3 to 10 years, and the deep water in 10 to 50 years.

## ICE IN THE SEA

Ice in the sea has two origins, the freezing of sea-water and the breaking of ice from glaciers. The majority of the ice comes from the first of these sources and will be referred to as *sea-ice*.

When sea-water freezes, needle-like crystals of pure ice form first, thereby increasing the salinity of the remaining liquid. However, as the crystals grow they tend to trap some of the concentrated salt solution ("brine") in pockets among them. The result is that new sea-ice (in bulk) is not pure $H_2O$ but has a salinity of 5 to 15‰. The faster the ice forms, the more saline is it likely to be. If this ice is lifted above sea level, as happens when the ice becomes thicker or when rafting occurs, the brine gradually trickles down through it and eventually leaves almost saltless, clear, old ice. Such ice, a year or more old, may be melted and used for drinking whereas new ice is not potable. Sea-ice must therefore be considered to be a material of variable composition and properties, which depend very much on its previous history.

The freezing point of sea-water decreases from 0°C at a salinity of 0‰ (fresh water) to −1·91°C at 35‰. An associated property is the temperature of maximum density which, at the surface, decreases from 3·94°C at a salinity of 0‰ to −1·33°C at a salinity of 24·7‰. At this temperature, the freezing point coincides with the temperature of maximum sea-water density, and the frequently tabulated values for the temperature of maximum density at higher salinities are below the freezing point and therefore meaningless.

The density of pure water at 0°C is 0·9999 g/cm³ and that of pure ice is 0·9168 g/cm³. However, the density of sea-ice may be greater than this last figure (if brine is trapped among the ice crystals) or less (if the brine has escaped and gas bubbles are present).

Values from 0·924 to 0·857 g/cm$^3$ were recorded on the Norwegian *Maud* Expedition.

Malmgren gives values for the specific heat of sea-ice of as much as 16 cal/g/C deg at −2°C and 15‰ salinity. This surprisingly high figure arises because the measurement of the specific heat requires heating over a finite range of temperature and there will be some melting of ice crystals into the brine. The 16 cal/g/C deg then includes some latent heat of melting and the high values are not true specific heats in the sense that the term is used for pure substances. The latent heat of melting decreases from the familiar 80 cal/g at 0°C and 0‰ salinity, to only 15 cal/g at −1°C and 15‰ salinity.

In the sea, incipient freezing is indicated by a "greasy" appearance of the sea surface due to the presence of flat ice crystals. As freezing continues, individual plates or spicules of ice develop in quantity ("frazil" ice) and these tend to aggregate to form "slush" ice. This slush then further aggregates to form "pancake" ice, flat rounded sheets of ½ m or more diameter. These then freeze together to form "floe" or "sheet" ice. Clear sheet ice such as forms on fresh water ponds does not form at sea. The rate of formation of ice depends very much on conditions. It is favoured by low salinity, lack of mixing by wind or currents, shallow water, and the presence of old ice which keeps the water calm. At a temperature of −30°C, 3 cm of ice can form in 1 hour and 30 cm in 3 days, the rate of increase of thickness diminishing as the ice thickness increases because ice is a poor conductor of heat. In Canadian Arctic waters a total of 2 to 3 m of ice may form inshore between September and May and then all melt by July.

In the *Arctic region* the sea-ice may be divided into three categories. The most extensive is the Polar Cap Ice which is always present and covers about 70% of the Arctic Sea, extending from the pole approximately to the 1000 m isobath (depth contour). It is very hummocky and on the average several years old. Some of this cap ice melts in the summer and the average thickness decreases to about 2½ m. Open water spaces, "polynyas", may form. In the autumn these freeze over and the ice in them gets squeezed into ridges, or pushed so that one piece slides up over another ("rafting"). In the winter the average ice thickness is 3 to $3\frac{1}{2}$ m but hummocks increase the height locally up to 10 m above sea level with increases in depth below sea level of four to five times this. The hummocks build up as the result of inward forces on ice sheets causing them to buckle or raft. The occasional ice islands which have fairly uniform thickness considerably greater than the regular cap ice originate from glaciers in northern Ellesmere Island.

Although this polar cap ice is always present it is not always the same ice. Up to one-third of the total cap and pack ice is carried away in the East Greenland Current each year while other ice is added from the pack ice described below. The polar cap ice circulates in a clockwise direction about a centre somewhere between the pole and Northern Canada. The motion is not smooth, but irregular or zig-zag because the cap ice does not move as a solid mass but, under the influence of changing wind stresses, its velocity varies and it shears. The polar cap is essentially impenetrable even by heavy ice-breakers.

The Pack Ice lies outside the polar cap and covers about 25% of the Arctic area. It is lighter than the cap ice and its area varies somewhat from year to year but extends usually to about the 1000 m isobath. It penetrates farther south in the East Greenland and the Labrador Currents by which it is carried. Its areal extent is least in September and greatest in May. Some of it melts in summer and some gets added to the cap by rafting. The pack ice can be penetrated by ice-breakers.

Lastly, the Fast Ice is that which forms from the shore out to the pack. This ice is "fast" or anchored to the shore and extends out to about the 20 m isobath. In the winter it develops to a thickness of 1 to 2 m but breaks up and melts completely in the summer. When it breaks away from the shore it may have beach material frozen into it and this may be carried some distance before being dropped as the ice melts.

The ice which prevents or impedes navigation in the northern parts of the Canadian Archipelago, along the east coast of Greenland, in Baffin Bay, Labrador Sea area and in the Bering Sea is the pack ice. It is of only a few metres thickness; separate pieces are called "floes" and should not be referred to as "icebergs".

The *icebergs* which are a menace to ships in the North Atlantic and in the Antarctic originate as pieces "calving" (i.e. breaking) off glaciers. In the North Atlantic the majority of the icebergs come from the glaciers of the west coast of Greenland and the east coast of Ellesmere Island. Icebergs differ from pack ice both in their origin on land and in their much greater vertical extent. When calved off the Greenland glaciers they frequently extend to 70 m above sea level but this height decreases rapidly thereafter. They are eventually carried south in the Labrador Current and some pass into the North Atlantic off Newfoundland. Here they are usually a few tens of metres high, the highest recorded being about 80 m high and the longest about 500 m. The density of their ice is about $0.90$ g/cm$^3$, a little less than that of pure ice because of the gas bubble content. The ratio of volume below sea level to that above sea level is close to 7 to 1 but the ratio of maximum depth below sea level to height above is less than this depending on the shape of the iceberg. It varies from 5 to 1 for a blocky shaped berg to only 1 to 1 for very irregular bergs.

The drift of icebergs is determined chiefly by the water currents, whereas the shallower pack ice is more directly influenced by the wind stress. This does not mean that the pack ice moves in the direction of the wind. In the northern hemisphere it moves significantly to the right of the wind direction due to the effect of the Coriolis force. The fact of the movement to the right of the wind was known to sailors long before it was explained scientifically by Nansen on a qualitative basis and, at his suggestion, by Ekman on a quantitative basis (see *Dynamical Oceanography*).

In the *Southern Ocean*, the immediately available information on the distribution of ice is not great, although in recent years a considerable amount of material must have been gathered but is not yet collated. On the basis of available data it appears that icebergs may be found to between 50 and 40°S while pack ice extends only to 65 to 60°S.  The relatively zonal distribution is probably due to the character of the currents in the Southern Ocean. An outstanding feature of the Antarctic is the Ross Ice Barrier with a sea front of about 700km to the Pacific and a height of 35 to 90m above sea level with a corresponding depth below.  This "shelf" ice represents the extension of the glaciers on the Antarctic continent out on to the sea where they float until bergs break off. These bergs may be up to 80 to 100km long and tens of kilometres wide.

In the *North Pacific Ocean* itself, ice does not occur, but it is formed in the adjacent seas to the north and west, the Bering Sea, the Sea of Okhotsk and the north of the Sea of Japan.  In the Bering Sea pack ice extends in winter to about 58°N but clears completely in the summer, retreating through the Bering Strait to about 70°N.

## PACIFIC OCEAN

Our oceanographic knowledge of the Pacific Ocean is less complete in some respects than that of the Atlantic.  The North Pacific can be described well, and our information on the currents in the Equatorial Pacific is more complete than that for the Equatorial Atlantic.  However, data on the South Pacific are sparse and it is not possible to describe it as adequately as the South Atlantic.

The *circulation in the upper waters* in the Pacific (Fig. 27) as a whole is very similar in its main features to that of the Atlantic. There is a clockwise gyre in the North Pacific and a counterclockwise one in the South Pacific.  The North and South Equatorial Currents form parts of the two gyres, and between them is an eastward flowing Equatorial Counter Current.  The whole equatorial current system is well and clearly developed in the Pacific and it will be described first, and the details of the two gyres given later.

The Pacific Equatorial Current system has long been known to consist of a well developed westward flowing South Equatorial

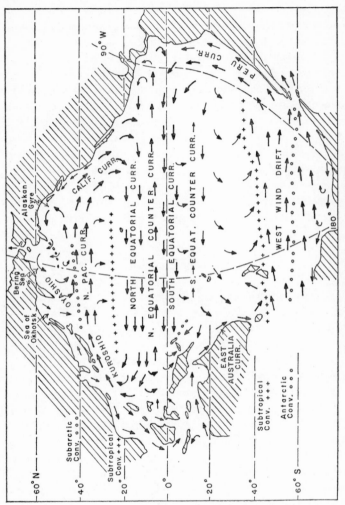

Fig. 27. Pacific Ocean—surface circulation.

Current between about 8 to 10°S and 3°N, a well developed west-ward flowing North Equatorial Current from about 8° to 20°N, and between these a narrower Equatorial Counter Current flowing to the east. This system can be traced from the Gulf of Panama in the east almost to the Philippines in the west, a distance of some 12,000km. The system is driven by the trade winds and is un-symmetrical about the equator because the trade wind system is unsymmetrical. To the south of the Hawaiian Islands the volume transport of the North Equatorial Current is about 45sv and the surface speeds are of the order of 25 to 30cm/sec. The South Equatorial Current is well known as a surface current to the west with surface speeds of the order of 50 to 65cm/sec but there is little information about its volume transport. Both of these currents show some seasonal variation of speed and position but are consistent in their direction to the west. The eastward flowing Equatorial Counter Current is more variable than the two previous ones. The surface speed is from 35 to 60cm/sec except in March and April when it decreases to 20cm/sec or less. In 1958, measurements at 107°W showed the Counter Current to extend through the thermo-cline to depths of some 1500m. If this pattern were character-istic of the full width of the Current it would indicate a total transport to the east of 60sv, twice the previously accepted figure of 30sv for the upper layers only. However, in 1959 at about 120°W, the small eastward transport in the upper 125m was balanced by a westward transport between this depth and 1500m with a resultant total transport of only 1sv, a remarkable change from the previous year.

These three currents complete the classical picture of the equa-torial current systems, but in recent years we have become aware of two further components. In the order of their discovery they are the Equatorial Undercurrent or Cromwell Current at the equator beneath the South Equatorial Current, and a South Equatorial Counter Current at 10 to 12°S.

The latter was first described in 1959 by Reid who had located it as a geostrophic flow by methods of dynamical oceanography. This current had not previously been recognized as it is narrow and not strong. For this reason and also because direct observations of currents are few in the South Pacific, particularly in the east, this current does not appear on atlases of sea surface currents. With the discovery of this South Equatorial Counter Current it will be necessary to refer to the earlier recognized one as the North Equatorial Counter Current.

The Equatorial Undercurrent is almost as large in volume transport as the North or South Equatorial Undercurrents and it lies only 100 m or less below the sea surface along the equator, yet it was not discovered until 1952. The programme of the Pacific Oceanic Fisheries Investigation of the U.S. Fish and Wildlife Service included systematic studies of the equatorial regions. In the summer of 1952 a cruise planned for detailed study at 150°W included current measurements by free drifting drogues at and below the surface at 3°S, on the equator and at 7°N. The outstanding result from the drogue measurements, announced by Cromwell, Montgomery and Stroup, was that near the equator and embedded in the well-known westward flowing South Equatorial Current there was a previously undiscovered eastward flowing current between 70 and 200m depth. An intensive study by Knauss, of Scripps Institution of Oceanography, revealed many details of the current. It is a thin ribbon, only 0·2km thick but 300km wide, extending from about 2°N to 2°S. In length it extends certainly from 150°W to 92°W (just east of the Galapagos Islands), a distance of 6500km, and there is evidence that it may start farther east and be more than 12,000km long. Even in the ocean in which features are typically thin, i.e. small in depth relative to their horizontal dimensions, a current with a thickness to width ratio of 1 to 1500 is remarkable, particularly when it retains its integrity for 6000 to 12,000km. The speed at the core of the current is up to 150cm/sec and the core rises from 100m depth at 150°W to 40m near the Galapagos, and may even break surface at times in the eastern Pacific. The volume transport is fairly steady at 40sv which approaches that of the Gulf Stream. In other words, it is a major ocean current which was unknown before 1952 and had not even been predicted by theory. In the 1958 study, the current was followed to just west of the Galapagos Islands but was not found east of them. At present it is not known exactly what does happen to the current at its eastern end but steps are being taken to find out. It is possible that it turns into the surface equatorial system but in what manner remains to be determined.

Once the existence of the Equatorial Undercurrent had been recognized in the Pacific it was realized that there had been strong indications of its existence for some time previously. These were in the form of strikingly large wire-angles from the vertical when oceanographic gear was being lowered over the side of ships when near the equator. These wire angles were toward the east and were attributed to the strong, shallow surface current (South Equatorial Current) carrying the ship toward the west relative to weaker or zero currents below the surface layer. It was only after the Undercurrent had been observed directly that these observations, together with the observations that at times floating fishing gear drifted toward the east, were recognized as being due to an eastward flowing Undercurrent.

The discovery of the Pacific Equatorial Undercurrent naturally started speculation as to the possibility of there being one in the Atlantic. In 1961, observational evidence from 1959 was presented to demonstrate the existence of such a current in the eastern equatorial Atlantic. About the same time it was pointed out that this Atlantic Equatorial Undercurrent had been clearly observed and recognized as such in 1886 by Buchanan, one of the scientists who had earlier taken part in the *Challenger* expedition. Buchanan's accounts were published in well-known geographical journals but had apparently been forgotten until the independent discovery of the Equatorial Undercurrent in the Pacific stimulated a review of the literature. It has been suggested that some remarks criticizing the validity of Buchanan's methods, made in Krümmel's *Handbuch der Ozeanographie* which carried much authority early in the century, may have diverted attention from Buchanan's observations.

Incidentally, the search for an equatorial undercurrent in the Atlantic was done for other reasons than to permit the Atlantic oceanographers to keep up with their Pacific colleagues. It was done more to assist in the search for an adequate dynamic explanation for the undercurrent at the equator. If an undercurrent were found both in the Pacific and in the Atlantic (and also in the Indian Ocean) it would suggest that it was a typical feature of the equatorial current system and that a common explanation might be adequate. Studies of the differences between the equatorial features as well as their similarities would help in deciding between alternative explanations. On the other hand, if the undercurrent were found only in the Pacific it might be that it was a consequence of some peculiarity of that ocean's circulation and this also might help in deciding on the most satisfactory explanation.

Since the equatorial current system is an interconnected one, the discovery of the new currents and the new measurements of the volume transports will require a reappraisal of the whole system.

One major distinction between the Pacific and the Atlantic equatorial current systems is that in the Pacific there is no major transport of upper water across the equator as is the case by the South Equatorial Current in the Atlantic.

The North Pacific Gyre may be considered to start with the North Equatorial Current which flows west and, on approaching the western boundary of the ocean, divides with some water going south to the North Equatorial Counter Current and some north (Fig. 27). This water continues north-east past Japan as a concentrated current called the Kuroshio which is the counterpart of the Florida Current in the Atlantic. After it leaves the Japanese coast to flow east it is called the Kuroshio Extension to about 170°E, corresponding to the Gulf Stream, and from there is referred to as the North Pacific Current. The volume transport of the Kuroshio Extension is about 65 sv, much the same as that of the Gulf Stream. Contributing to the North Pacific Current is the Oyashio, coming in from the north from the Bering Sea and with some contribution from the Sea of Okhotsk. As the North Pacific Current approaches the North American continent it divides. Part turns south as the California Current and eventually feeds into the North Equatorial

Current. The remainder swings north to form the Alaskan Gyre in the Gulf of Alaska, and then much of it flows between the Aleutian Islands into the Bering Sea. The position of the divergence of the

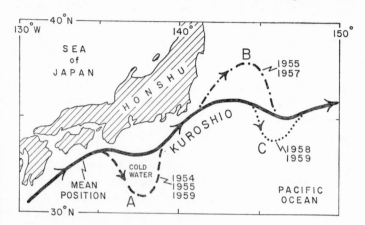

FIG. 28. *Kuroshio, mean position and fluctuations during 1954 to 1959 (after Masuzawa).*

North Pacific Current is at about 45°N in the winter and 50°N in the summer. The general pattern of the North Pacific circulation is similar to that in the Atlantic with a concentrated north-eastward flowing current on the west side while the southward return flow is spread across much of the remainder of the ocean.

Since 1954 systematic observations of the Kuroshio have been made four times a year by Japanese oceanographers and some interesting results have emerged. The GEK (Chapter 6) was used to determine the surface currents, supplemented by temperature observations below the surface. The current axis showed a distinct long term variation in position. In Fig. 28 the full line represents the average position of the current during 1954 to 1959 but this six year average conceals many changes. In 1954 and 1955 a great loop to the south developed in area A (Fig. 28), and in the region between it and the coast an unusual cold water mass appeared. In 1956 to

1958 the current moved back to the coast but in 1959 the loop to the south developed again and with it the inshore cold water mass. In 1955 and 1957 the current swung further north than the average in area B, while in 1958 to 1959 it swung farther south in area C. Several reasons for these long period changes and for the appearance of the cold water mass have been put forward but none is considered satisfactory. The maximum current speeds in the Kuroshio for the period ranged between 75 and 250 cm/sec while the width of the current in which the speed was over 100 cm/sec was less than 80 km most of the time. There seems to be some indication that the higher current speeds and the greater widths occurred together. If this is also characteristic of the deeper parts of the current it would imply considerable variations in the volume transport. The possible existence of a south-westward countercurrent below the Kuroshio, similar to that below the Gulf Stream, has already been mentioned.

The South Pacific Gyre is less well documented than that in the North Pacific. The South Equatorial Current forms the northern portion of this gyre and there is the East Australia Current on the west side, but it is much smaller in transport than the western boundary currents in the other oceans. The connection between these two currents in the western South Pacific is uncertain. In the south, the West Wind Drift of the Antarctic Circumpolar Circulation continues the gyre, and part of it turns north up the South American coast as the Peru Current. This current has been examined by several expeditions and the coastal side of it, at least, is well described. Its volume transport is only about one-third of that of the Gulf Stream or the Kuroshio. It turns to the west near the equator and contributes to the South Equatorial Current. The low temperature tongue extending west along the equator (Figs. 6 and 7) which looks like a continuation of the cool Peru Current was attributed by Sverdrup to upwelling of cool subsurface water associated with the divergence to be expected with a wind-driven current straddling the equator.

The Peru Current is an example of an eastern boundary current which is characteristically broad and slow, contrasting with the narrow and swift western boundary currents. The Peru Current flows equatorward and as it comes from high latitudes it is cool and of relatively low salinity. The upwelling (page 39), which occurs along this eastern boundary on account of the southerly winds, also brings cool water to the surface. The equatorward current is mostly above about 500 m depth. Below it there is a poleward current particularly along the Chilean coast. These features described for the ocean off Peru and Chile are found along other eastern boundaries of the oceans. One item of difference between regions is that while the upwelling always cools the surface layer, because temperature normally decreases downward, it may increase or decrease the surface salinity depending on whether salinity increases or decreases with depth in the locality.

Generally the Peru Current extends to a few degrees south of the equator before turning west and its low surface-water temperatures are in contrast with the higher temperatures north of it. The high temperatures extend farthest south during the southern summer, December to March. At intervals of a few years the high temperatures extend 5 to 10 degrees farther south than usual, a condition known as "El Niño". The increase in temperature kills many fish not tolerant of high temperatures. It is also accompanied by increased evaporation and consequent greater precipitation on the neighbouring land, so that floods cause much damage in this region where the normal rainfall is very small.

The earlier explanation for the extreme southward extent of high temperatures was that a southward flow of warm North Equatorial Counter Current water occurred. In 1960 Wooster suggested alternatively that the wind stress parallel to the coast decreased and in consequence there was decreased upwelling of cool water. This would permit the normal net heat inflow to raise the surface-water temperature higher than usual. The southward current of warm water would not be necessary with this explanation, although it is probable that some such flow does occur and contributes to the "El Niño" condition. A third suggestion, offered by Reid, is that the normally weak South Equatorial Counter Current may occasionally strengthen and carry warm water right to the coast. The fact is that our knowledge of the oceanographic conditions off the South American coast is not sufficiently detailed for us to say for certain whether only one of these mechanisms is responsible for the southward extension of higher temperatures or whether all contribute in different degree on different occasions.

Wooster and Stommel have further suggested that similar conditions to the "*El Niño*" probably occur annually off other upwelling coasts, such as those of California and Southwest Africa, when the equatorward winds die down seasonally. However, the consequences are small compared to those along the Peruvian coast where a significant seasonal decrease of wind is unusual.

The *water masses of the Pacific* are rather more complicated than those of the Atlantic, probably because the greater size of the Pacific provides more opportunity for different masses to develop and be maintained in different parts of the ocean.

At the surface, the salinity shows the typical maxima in the tropics with a minimum in the equatorial regions (Fig. 11), and with lower values at higher latitudes. The surface salinity in the North Pacific is considerably less than in the North Atlantic. In the South Pacific the average salinity is higher than in the North Pacific but slightly less than in the South Atlantic. The surface temperature (Figs. 6 and 7) shows the usual equatorial maximum, the highest values being in the west at the downstream end of the North and South Equatorial Currents. There is also the previously mentioned minimum along the equator in the east attributable to the effect of upwelling. Apart from the perturbation due to the Peru Current and some effect of upwelling along the mid-latitude shores of the American continent, the distribution of the isotherms is distinctly zonal.

The phenomenon of upwelling due to the wind stress as described in Chapter 4 is evident off the shores of both North and South America. Off the North American coast from British Columbia to California relatively cool water is usually found from April to August within a region 80 to 300 km wide from the shore (Fig. 6). The cold water is often patchy, rather than being in a uniform band, and comes from depths of no more than 300 m. Off the South American coast, upwelling has been observed between 5° and 35° S and comes from an average depth of 130 m with a maximum of 350 m.

It is in the upper water masses, below the surface layer, that the variety of water properties is found. Between depths of about 100 m and 800 m there are the North and South Pacific Central Water Masses and the Pacific Equatorial Water Mass (Fig. 22). The Equatorial Water extends from shore to shore, but despite this extent of approximately 12,000 km it has a very uniform [TS] diagram across the whole width of the ocean. In the eastern Pacific this Water extends from about 20° N to 10° S but diminishes in north-south extent to the west. Except for the western South Pacific water it is the most saline water in this ocean, but even so is slightly less saline than the Atlantic Central Waters. The Equatorial Water is separated from the well mixed and homogeneous surface layer by a very strong thermocline, and vertical transfer of water properties up or down is inhibited by the stability of the water. For this reason it is referred to as the "discontinuity layer". The depth of the discontinuity layer decreases from 150 to 200 m in the west to 50 m or less in the east; the layer even seems to reach the surface at times near the American coast. This effect is associated with the Costa Rican Thermal Dome, an apt name which describes the three-dimensional shape of the thermocline with the cold water of the lower thermocline occasionally penetrating to the sea surface itself.

At about the level of the thermocline in the Equatorial Waters is the salinity maximum which is characteristic of the equatorial regions (Fig. 12). It is of limited areal extent and so does not appear in Fig. 22 which shows averages over large areas. At about 800 m there is a slight salinity minimum which represents the limit of the northward influence of the Antarctic Intermediate Water.

The North Pacific Central Water extends from the Equatorial Water to about 40° N and is the least saline of the central water masses of the oceans. Sverdrup distinguished an extensive western North Pacific Central Water to the west of the Hawaiian Islands from a smaller eastern North Pacific Central Water between these Islands and the North American coast, though separated from the coast by another water mass. Examination of the accumulation of data for the North Pacific since 1955 has indicated that the two water masses are less easily distinguished now than they were with the lesser amount of data available to Sverdrup. They are not separated in Fig. 22a.

South of the Equatorial Water are the western and eastern South Pacific Central Water Masses extending to the Subtropical Convergence at 40°S which is usually considered as the oceanographic southern boundary of the Pacific Ocean. In the South Pacific the Central Water Masses are less easily distinguished from the Equatorial water than is the case in the North Pacific.

North of the North Pacific Central Water is a Pacific Subarctic Water Mass which extends across the greater part of the ocean. Its characteristic properties are low salinity (33·5 to 34·5‰) and relatively low temperature (2 to 4°C). It is a much more extensive and important water mass than the Atlantic Subarctic water. It corresponds to the Subantarctic Water in the south but its mode of formation must be somewhat different. The Subantarctic Water is formed between the Subtropical and the Antarctic Convergences which are essentially continuous across the South Pacific. In the North Pacific the Subarctic Convergence is only clear in the western part of the Pacific (Fig. 27) where the Subarctic Water must be formed by mixing between the warm, saline waters of the Kuroshio Extension and the cold, less saline waters of the Oyashio. In the eastern North Pacific there is certainly a gradation from Subarctic to Central Water but it is less easy to localize than is the Antarctic Convergence. The Subarctic Water forms a part of the North Pacific Current flowing to the east and it retains its characteristics of low salinity and temperature until it approaches the American coast. Here part of it swings south-east and its temperature starts to rise by heating and the salinity by mixing until it attains the typical Equatorial Water Mass characteristics as it merges into the North Equatorial Current.

Intermediate water masses are found below the Central waters in both the North and South Pacific. In the latter, the Antarctic Intermediate Water is formed by subsurface mixing at and north of the Antarctic Convergence with fairly well defined properties, a temperature close to $2.2°C$ and a salinity of $33.8\%_{00}$. This salinity is relatively low and so the Antarctic Intermediate Water gives rise to the minimum in the $[TS]$ diagram below the Subantarctic and the Central Waters (Fig. 22b). The Intermediate Water flows north, mixing up and down, but is limited in northward extent by the Pacific Equatorial Water. This contrasts with the situation in the Atlantic where, in the absence of a clearly defined Equatorial Water Mass, the Intermediate Water continues north across the equator. In the North Pacific an Intermediate Water, evident as a salinity minimum, is found below the North Pacific Central Water (Fig. 22a). In the west it is deepest at about 800 m but rises to the east to about 300 m. It appears to circulate in a clockwise gyre, similar to the surface water, and its relatively high oxygen content indicates frequent replenishment. Sverdrup suggested that it is formed in the west near Japan by sinking at the convergence of the Oyashio and the Kuroshio Extension. Reid has pointed out that the salinity minimum of the North Pacific Intermediate Water occurs on a surface of constant density $\sigma_t = 26.8$ and that water of this density does not occur at the surface in the North Pacific at any time. Where this density is found at the surface in the South Pacific, the salinity is higher than in the salinity minimum of the North Pacific Intermediate Water. Reid therefore concludes that this latter water attains its properties below the surface by vertical mixing in the Subarctic region where the particular density surface is shallow and the surface waters above are cold, low in salinity and high in oxygen content. If the North Pacific Intermediate Water is indeed formed in this way it is one of the few exceptions, with the Antarctic Intermediate Water, to the general rule that subsurface water masses acquire their $[TS]$ characteristics at the surface of the sea.

The *Deep Water of the Pacific* is characterized by very uniform properties as may be seen in the longitudinal sections in Fig. 29.

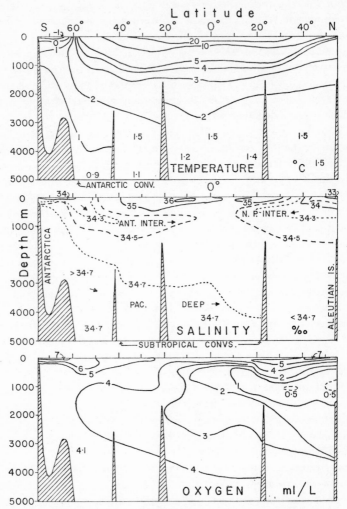

FIG. 29. *South–north longitudinal sections of water characteristics in the Pacific Ocean along 175° W (after Muromtsev).*

Between 2000m and the bottom the temperature range (as far south as the Subtropical Convergence) is only from 1·1 to 2·2°C and the salinity from 34·65 to 34·75‰. The salinity tends to increase with depth from about 2000m or to remain constant, in contrast to the situation in the Atlantic where there is the marked salinity maximum of the North Atlantic Deep Water at mid-depth with a decrease to lower values in the Bottom Water (Fig. 23). A partial reason for the uniformity in the Pacific Ocean is that no deep water is formed in it, north or south, and the ocean is essentially a sink for waters from the other oceans. In the north, the surface salinity is too low for winter cooling to make the water dense enough to sink to any considerable depth. Even in the Pacific sector of the Antarctic no significant amount of deep or bottom water is formed.

The Pacific Deep and Bottom Water from 2500m down must be supplied entirely from the Antarctic circumpolar current. It spreads north at 160 to 180°W and, after crossing the equator, branches north-west and north-east along basins into the North Pacific. The flow is probably fastest on the west side; the speeds are estimated by Knauss to be of the order of 0·1 cm/sec and the transport as 15 to 25 sv. The evidence for the flow pattern is the gradual increase in temperature along the route, from about 0.9°C in the Antarctic to 1·5 to 1·6°C in the North Pacific, and a small decrease in oxygen content (Fig. 29). There is a slight indication of decrease in salinity into the North Pacific but the change is close to the limits of measurement accuracy. The rise of temperature is attributed to heat flow from the interior of the earth into the sea. The water which penetrates into the North Pacific must rise into the upper layers above 2000m.

Sverdrup considered, essentially by analogy with the Atlantic, that a slow southward movement of deep water (i.e. between the Bottom Water and the Intermediate Water) must occur in the South Pacific. This southward movement of deep water would be supplied from the northward movement of Bottom Water below it and the Intermediate Water above. The indications are, therefore, that the deep and bottom water movements in the Pacific are very slow, and that there is only a small exchange between North and South Pacific in contrast to the large volume exchange at various levels across the equator in the Atlantic.

The deep waters of the Pacific and of the Indian Ocean are very similar and in his analysis of the distribution of temperature and salinity Montgomery pointed out that this water, with its mean temperature of $1 \cdot 5°\,C$ and salinity of $34 \cdot 70‰$, forms the largest water mass in the world ocean. For this reason he named it the "(Oceanic) Common Water" from which other water masses are distinguished by differences of temperature and salinity. The Common Water has average properties because it is a mixture of other masses chiefly North Atlantic Deep and Antarctic Bottom Waters with some admixture from the Indian and Pacific Oceans.

Although the large body of deep water in the Pacific is usually called the Pacific Deep Water, the name in this case indicates the region where the mass is found, rather than where it is formed, as is often the case with water mass names.

Comparison of Fig. 29 with Fig. 23 will show that in addition to differing from the Atlantic in being more uniform in temperature and salinity distribution, the Pacific water also has lower dissolved oxygen values. In the Atlantic the values range from 3 to $6 \cdot 5\,ml/l$ in the deep water, whereas they are from $0 \cdot 5$ to $4 \cdot 5\,ml/l$ in the Pacific. These lower values are consistent with the presumed greater age and slower circulation of the deep water in the Pacific, or perhaps it would be better to say that they are one of the reasons for believing the circulation to be slow. In the eastern Pacific, between $10°$ and $20°\,N$, there is a core of remarkably low values down to less than $0 \cdot 1\,ml/l$ between 200 and 1000 m. There is probably a similar region off Peru. Below these oxygen minimum layers in the upper waters the values rise again in the deep water. Corresponding to the general low oxygen values are high concentrations of nutrients, particularly in the North Pacific. Values of 2 to $3 \cdot 5\,\mu g$ atom/l of phosphorus as phosphate are typical in the North Pacific compared to values of $0 \cdot 5$ to $2\,\mu g$ atom/l in the Atlantic. Similar large concentrations of dissolved nitrate and silicate are also found in the North

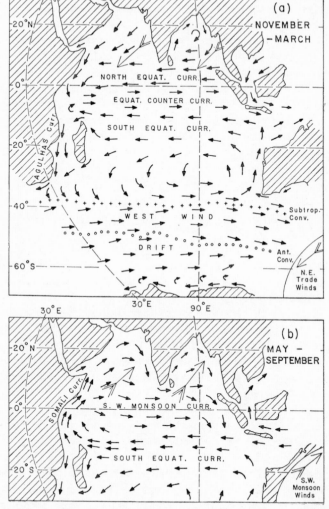

FIG. 30.  *Indian Ocean—surface circulation.*

Pacific waters. These materials go into solution during the decomposition of organic matter, e.g. dead plankton. High concentrations may be the result of a copious supply of organic remains from life in the upper waters, or may accumulate as a consequence of the slow movement of the deep water. In the case of the Pacific, the latter is assumed to be the main cause.

One feature which is lacking in the Pacific, as compared to the Atlantic and the Indian Oceans, is a source of high salinity, warm water such as comes from the European Mediterranean and from the Red Sea respectively. These water masses are not of major importance in terms of volume but are very useful as tracers of the movement of subsurface waters.

## INDIAN OCEAN AND RED SEA

The *Indian Ocean* differs from the Atlantic and the Pacific in its limited northward extent. The Subtropical Convergence at about 40°S is usually considered as the southern boundary of the Indian Ocean.

The *surface circulation* in the southern Indian Ocean (Fig. 30a) consists of a counter-clockwise gyre, as in the other southern oceans, bounded on the south by the West Wind Drift. A part of this turns north past the west coast of Australia, being supplemented by a coastal flow south of that continent, and turns into the South Equatorial Current.

It is in the equatorial current system that the Indian Ocean circulation differs most from that in the Atlantic and the Pacific. As a consequence of the seasonal changes of wind conditions resulting from the land mass to the north of the ocean, there is a marked seasonal variation in the equatorial current system which does not occur in the other two oceans. During the period from November to March the system is similar to that in the other oceans, with two westward flowing currents and a counter current between them (Fig. 30a). The whole system, however, is farther south than in the Atlantic and Pacific. The South Equatorial Current extends across the ocean between 20°S and 8°S; it varies in speed with variations in the south-east trade winds but continues to the west throughout the year. North of this, the Equatorial Counter Current flows east from 8°S and 2°S, while the North Equatorial Current flows west between 2°S and 6 to 10°N. During this period (November to March) the north-east trade winds blow and maintain the North Equatorial Current. However, starting in April there is a complete change in the wind system north of the equator and the north-east trade winds (north-east monsoon) are replaced by winds from the south-west, (south-west monsoon). These are really a continuation across the equator of the south-east trade winds. With this change of wind the North Equatorial Current to the west is replaced by a south-west Monsoon Current to the east and the Equatorial Counter Current disappears or becomes indistinguishable from the Monsoon Current (Fig. 30b). This situation continues from May until September when the south-west monsoon dies away and the North Equatorial Current reappears as the north-east trade winds return.

That this seasonal variation in the North Equatorial Current is associated with the change of wind is well known, and it is known that the current change takes place fairly quickly after the wind change. However, quantitative details of the change of current in relation to the change of wind are scarce, and one of the objects of the physical oceanographic programme of the International Indian Ocean Expedition during 1962 to 1965 was to investigate them. This Expedition was an extensive oceanographic study of the Indian Ocean, as one of the least-known oceans, covering the whole ocean and extending over 2 to 3 years so that some estimate of the extent and significance of seasonal and annual variations might be obtained. Many nations cooperated in order that the observations might be as nearly synoptic, i.e. simultaneous, as possible. This Indian Ocean region is the only one in the open ocean where such a considerable change in wind takes place regularly and it is anticipated that the field observations of related wind and current change will prove to be of fundamental importance to physical oceanography. In other regions, wind variations take place but they are not so radical as those in the north Indian Ocean and consequently it is not easy to relate them to variations in the local currents.

Knauss and Taft have observed that an Equatorial Undercurrent occurs in the Indian Ocean. The Undercurrent was found only to the east of 60°E and increased in speed to the most easterly current station at 92°E. It was strongest at the end of the north-east monsoon (April) but was observed also during the south-west monsoon (July and September). The speed of the Indian Equatorial Undercurrent was only about one half that of the Undercurrents in the Pacific and Atlantic, and also it was more variable than these.

During the north-east monsoon period the South Equatorial Current, when it reaches the African shore, supplies both the Equatorial Counter Current to its north and the Agulhas Current flowing south (Fig. 30a). This current is remarkably narrow, probably only 100km wide, and flows south close to the African shore. When it reaches the southern tip of Africa, most of the current turns east into the West Wind Drift of the Circumpolar Current. During the south-west monsoon, when the Equatorial Counter Current disappears, the component of the South Equatorial Current which turns north supplies the Somali Current up the east coast of Africa (Fig. 30b). This current is notable for its high speeds of up to 200cm/sec which are comparable to those in the Florida Current.

The surface *water masses* in the open *Indian Ocean* have typical characteristics, a substantially zonal distribution of the isotherms with a temperature maximum near the equator (Figs. 6 and 7), and a salinity maximum at about 30°S in the eastern ocean (Fig. 11). This is somewhat farther south than in the Atlantic and Pacific. In the north, the Arabian Sea west of India and the Bay of Bengal to the east have very different characteristics. The Arabian Sea has high surface salinity values up to 36·5‰, while in the Bay of Bengal the salinity decreases from about 34‰ at about 5°N to 31‰

or less in the north. The low values in the Bay of Bengal are due to the very considerable river runoff into it, particularly during the south-west monsoon.

Below the surface (Fig. 21b) is the Indian Equatorial Water north of 10°S, with only a small range of salinity from 34·9 to 35·2‰, and the Indian Central Water which has a greater range of salinity and is very similar to the South Atlantic Central Water. The Indian Equatorial Water extends to about 2000 m depth and the Central to 800 to 1000 m. Below the Central Water is the Antarctic Intermediate Water with its usual salinity minimum.

In recent years, a considerable amount of data has been acquired in the Indian Ocean by various research expeditions but little analysis of it has yet been published. Earlier data, particularly for the south-east Indian Ocean, is sparse and it is difficult to present an adequate description of the Deep Water beyond stating that it has a rather limited range of temperature (1° to 3°C) and of salinity (34·6 to 34·8‰). With the Pacific Deep Water it forms a part of Montgomery's Common Water.

The *Red Sea* contributes a warm, saline subsurface water descending to 1000 to 1500 m depth in the western Indian Ocean. The depths in the Red Sea average about 1000 m with basins to over 2200 m, while there is a sill of about 125 m depth toward the south end. Because of the very dry climate, evaporation exceeds precipitation and there is no river runoff into the Red Sea. In consequence, high salinities occur, up to 42·5‰ at the north end, combined with high temperatures. Summer temperatures of the Red Sea surface water range up to 30°C and winter ones down to 18°C. The main body of Deep Water below sill depth is very uniform at 21·7°C and 40·6‰. This water is formed in the winter at the north end of the Sea. Neumann and McGill in 1961 presented evidence to show that the water which flows out of the Red Sea into the Indian Ocean is not the deep basin water, but water recently cooled at the surface and flowing to the mouth in a shallow layer at and above the 125 m sill depth. As a result, the water which leaves the Red Sea is rather different in properties from the Red

Sea Deep Water.  Inside the sill it is at about 24°C and 39·8‰, but during its flow over the sill into the Indian Ocean mixing reduces these values to 15°C and 36‰.  The subsurface outflow is, of course, compensated by a surface inflow from the Indian Ocean.  This exchange with the outside ocean is very similar to that which Wüst has described for the Mediterranean, particularly in respect of the outflow being from the upper layers and not due to displacement of deep basin water.  From such data as is available the Red Sea water appears to flow south in the Indian Ocean but it cannot be followed as far as the Mediterranean water in the Atlantic.  However, the present available data is scanty and we are likely to get a much better understanding of the Red Sea water distribution from the results of the International Indian Ocean Expedition.

# CHAPTER EIGHT

# Coastal Oceanography

OCEANOGRAPHIC conditions in coastal waters differ in many respects from those in the open sea. In particular, variations with position and with time are larger. Some of the factors causing these differences are river runoff, tidal currents and the effect of shore boundaries on circulation. Many of the world's fisheries are in coastal waters, and other problems such as those concerned with the disposal of sewage or industrial effluent are of immediate importance. Some of the characteristics of coastal oceanography will therefore be described.

The effect of the shore as a boundary in limiting possible directions of flow is obvious. It is important to recognize this effect because it represents one of the few situations in which man can exert a significant influence on the ocean. Jetties and breakwaters, designed for the protection of shipping from swell, may also redirect currents. In the past this has often led to unexpected changes such as the deposition of silt and the formation of new shoals, or the removal of beaches when a jetty prevented the longshore movement of sand required to maintain a beach whose material was being eroded away by wave action.

The effects of tidal currents are twofold. They may cause large changes twice daily in the volume of water in a harbour or bay, and they may also promote vertical mixing and thus break down the stratification in the water. For instance, where there are strong tidal currents over a rough bottom in shallow water the heat absorbed in the surface layer may be mixed through a considerable depth.

A result will be lower surface temperatures compared to those toward the head of a bay nearby where the currents are slight.

The direct effect of river runoff is to reduce the salinity of the surface layers, and even of the deeper water if there is sufficient vertical mixing. Generally, river runoff has a pronounced seasonal variation and this gives rise to much larger seasonal fluctuations in salinity in coastal waters than in the open ocean. In a coastal region where precipitation occurs chiefly as rain, the seasonal salinity variation will follow closely the local precipitation pattern. In regions where rivers are fed by melt water from snow fields or glaciers, the river runoff increases in the summer to many times the winter rate and causes a corresponding decrease in salinity during this period. Since river water frequently carries suspended sediment this causes the coastal waters to have low optical transparency. Sometimes this sediment is carried in the surface low-salinity layer for some time while the deeper, more saline, water remains relatively clear. The deposition of this sediment causes shoaling and consequent hazards to navigation. Frequently the location of this deposition is influenced by the salinity distribution because increases in salinity can cause flocculation of the sediment and rapid settling.

In low latitude regions, where precipitation is slight, evaporation becomes important and high salinities as well as high temperatures occur in bays and partially surrounded bodies of sea-water.

Along the continental shelf, variations in water conditions may be important to fish populations. Sometimes these variations are seasonal in character, but important longer term variations have also been recorded. For instance, cod appear to have a limited tolerance to water temperature and the yield of the cod fishery off West Greenland has been shown to be very sensitive to this factor. A great improvement in the yield occurred from 1924 on, when the water temperature rose from below 0° to 1°C. Previously rich fisheries had been experienced in 1845 to 1850 when there was less ice than usual and presumably higher temperatures (water temperatures are not available for that time), but the yield had declined thereafter.

When carrying out oceanographic surveys in coastal waters it is necessary to take into account the special characteristics of these regions. Because of the large variations with position of oceanographic properties it is necessary to arrange oceanographic stations closer together than in the open ocean. For instance, in the open ocean a minimum spacing of 50 to 100km may be adequate but near the coast it may be necessary to reduce this to 5 or 10km or even less. In addition, seasonal variations are much greater near shore and in order to obtain a complete picture of oceanographic conditions it is necessary to extend observations over one or more full years. In doing this a number of oceanographic cruises are necessary because single winter and summer cruises will usually be insufficient to describe the full range of water characteristics and the time and extent of changeover periods between the winter and summer extremes. Since tidal currents play an important part, it is desirable also to plan time-series observations over one or more tidal days (25 hours) at key locations. It is not uncommon to find as large variations in 25 hours at a single location in coastal waters as occur over distances of 50 to 100km simultaneously in the same region.

The extreme of coastal conditions is often found in and near river mouths and estuaries, and some of the features of such regions are described below.

## ESTUARIES

Oceanographically the term "estuary" has a wider meaning than the conventional one of the tidal region at the mouth of a large river. Cameron and Pritchard define an estuary as "a semi-enclosed coastal body of water having a free connection to the open sea and within which sea-water is measurably diluted with fresh water deriving from land drainage." They restrict the definition to coastal features and exclude large bodies of water such as the Baltic Sea. The river water which enters the estuary mixes to some extent with the salt water therein and eventually flows out to the open sea in the upper layer. A corresponding inflow of sea-water takes place below the upper layer. The inflow and outflow are dynamically associated so that while an increase in river flow tends to reduce the salinity of the estuary water it also causes an increased inflow of sea-water which tends to increase it. Thus an approximate steady state prevails.

In terms of shape, Pritchard distinguishes three types, the coastal plain, the deep basin and the bar-built estuary. The first of these is the result of land subsidence or a rise of sea-level flooding a river valley; examples are the St. Lawrence River valley and Chesapeake Bay in North America. The most typical examples of the second type are the fjords of Norway, Greenland, Canada, South America and New Zealand. Most of these have a sill or region toward the seaward end which is shallower than both the main basin and the sea outside and so restricts the exchange of deep water. The third type is the narrow channel between the shore and a bar which has built up close to it by sedimentation or wave action. The inland end of an estuary is called the "head" and the seaward end the "mouth". Positive estuaries have a river or rivers emptying into them, usually at the head, and it is this which gives rise to the characteristic features of water property distributions in such estuaries.

Estuaries have been classified by Stommel in terms of the distribution of water properties as (a) vertically mixed, (b) slightly stratified, (c) highly stratified and (d) salt wedge estuaries. The stratification referred to is of salinity, because it is typical of estuaries that the density of the water is determined mainly by the salinity rather than by temperature. The salinity distributions in these four types are shown in Fig. 31 in two ways. In the left hand column of graphs the property distributions are shown as vertical profiles of salinity at each of four stations between the head and the mouth of the estuary as shown in the schematic plan view at the top. The right hand column shows simplified longitudinal sections of salinity from head to mouth for the full depth of the estuary.

The vertically mixed estuary (type A, Fig. 31) is shallow and the water is mixed vertically so that it is homogeneous from top to

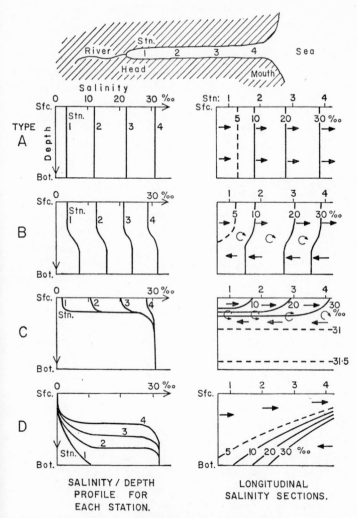

SALINITY / DEPTH
PROFILE FOR
EACH STATION.

LONGITUDINAL
SALINITY SECTIONS.

FIG. 31. *Typical salinity/depth profiles and longitudinal salinity
sections in estuaries.*

bottom at any particular place along the estuary. The salinity increases with distance along the estuary from head to mouth. The river water in such an estuary flows toward the mouth while the salt may be considered to progress from the sea toward the head by eddy diffusion at all depths. In the right hand figure the vertical isohalines indicate the homogeneity of the water at each location while the arrows indicate that the direction of net flow of water is seaward at all depths. The Severn River in England is an example.

In the slightly stratified estuary (type B), which is also usually shallow, the salinity increases from head to mouth at all depths. the water is essentially in two layers with the upper layer a little less saline than the deeper one at each position, with a mixing layer between them. In this type of estuary there is a net seaward or outward flow in the upper layer and a net inward flow in the deeper layer as shown in the salinity section. In addition to this flow at both levels there is vertical mixing both of fresh and of salt water giving rise to the the longitudinal variation of salinity in both layers. The circular arrows in the salinity section are intended to indicate this mixing. The James River in Chesapeake Bay is an example.

In the highly stratified estuary (type C), of which the fjords are typical, the upper layer increases in salinity from about zero in the river at the head to a value close to that of the outside sea at the mouth. The deep water, however, is of almost uniform salinity from head to mouth. Again there is a net outflow in the upper layer and inflow in the deeper water as shown by the arrows in the salinity section. In these estuaries there is a very strong halocline between the upper water and the deep water, particularly at the head where vertical salinity gradients of 10 to 20‰/m may occur in summer during the period of greatest river runoff. There is vertical mixing but this results predominantly in an upward movement of salt water from below into the upper layer, with little downward movement of fresh water. There is no satisfactory explanation yet for this predominantly one directional mixing.

A feature of the stratified estuaries is that the depth of the halo-cline, i.e. the thickness of the upper (low salinity) layer, remains substantially the same from head to mouth of the estuary for a given river runoff. If the estuary width does not change much, the constancy of depth of the upper layer means that the cross-sectional area of the upper layer outflow remains the same while its volume transport increases because of the entrainment of salt water from below. In consequence the speed of the outflowing surface layer increases markedly along the inlet from head to mouth. The increase in volume and speed can be very considerable, the outflow at the mouth being as much as 10 to 30 times the volume of the river flow. In his classical study of Alberni Inlet, a typical highly-stratified fjord-type estuary in British Columbia, Tully demonstrated the above features. He also showed that the depth of the upper zone decreased as the river runoff increased up to a critical value and thereafter increased as the runoff increased.

The circulation described, with outflow of the upper layer and inflow below it, is referred to as an "estuarine" circulation and has to be considered when practical problems of disposing of sewage or of industrial effluent are under consideration. The circulation is dependent on several factors, among them the sill depth, the river runoff and the character of the outside water density distribution. If the sill is so shallow that it penetrates into the low-salinity outflowing upper layer the full estuarine circulation cannot develop and the inflow of deep saline water does not occur regularly. In consequence the deep water is not exchanged and tends to become stagnant. This situation occurs in some of the smaller Norwegian fjords but it is by no means typical of deep basin estuaries. A large proportion of the Norwegian fjords and almost all of those on the Canadian west coast have sills which are deeper than the upper layer. In consequence the estuarine circulation is developed sufficiently to effect continual renewal of the deep water so that complete stagnation does not occur. The rate of renewal is proportional to the circulation which is itself proportional to the river runoff. Fjord estuaries with small river-runoff show more evidence of limited

7

circulation in the form of low oxygen values than do those with large river-runoff. The depth of the sill has little effect as long as it is greater than the depth of the low-salinity outflowing upper layer.

The other factor which may have some effect on the exchange of the deep basin water is a seasonal variation in density structure of the outside sea-water. Although the downward mixing of river water is small it does occur to some extent. In consequence the salinity, and therefore the density, of the basin water tends to decrease slowly. If a change then occurs in the outside water such that the density outside becomes greater than that inside at similar levels above the sill depth, there will be an inflow of water from the sea. The inflowing water is likely to sink, although not necessarily to the bottom, in the estuary basin and so displace upward and outward some of the previously resident water. In this way the basin water becomes refreshed. In deep-sill estuaries this refreshment may occur annually, but in shallow sill estuaries it may occur only at intervals of many years and the disturbance to the biological regime in the estuary may be cataclysmic on these occasions. It is this type of basin-water replacement which has been well documented for the Norwegian fjords with very shallow sills, but it should not be considered to be characteristic of all fjord estuaries.

For the salt wedge estuary (type D) the longitudinal section indicates the reason for its name. The saline water intrudes from the sea as a wedge below the river water. This situation usually occurs in rivers of large volume transport such as the Mississippi or the Fraser River. It should be noted that as usual the section in Fig. 31 is exaggerated in the vertical direction; the salt wedge is really a very thin one so that the isohalines are in fact almost horizontal.

The salt wedge estuary has features in common with the stratified estuaries. There is a horizontal gradient of salinity at the bottom as in the slighly stratified estuary and a pronounced vertical salinity gradient as in the highly stratified estuary. The distinction is in the lack of salinity gradient at the surface, the water there being fresh or nearly so until it debouches into the sea at the estuary mouth. This is because of the very large flow.

The above remarks should be regarded only as a brief description of some of the salient characteristics of estuaries. The discussion in detail of the circulation is a matter for the dynamical oceanographer and will not be considered here. The mechanics of the process of mixing between fresh and salt water, in which the tidal movements appear to play a large part, are in the same category and much research remains to be done in this field.

It should also be pointed out that estuarine characteristics and processes are observed in ocean areas as well as by the coast. In the north-east Pacific and in the Bay of Bengal where there is considerable river-runoff, the density of the upper layer is controlled by the salinity rather than by temperature as is usually the case in the open ocean. The upper, low-salinity layer of perhaps 100m depth in the north-east Pacific is less dense than the deeper, more saline water and the stability of the water between them inhibits mixing. In consequence the summer input of heat is trapped in the surface layer and a marked seasonal thermocline develops as shown in Fig. 9. In the Arctic Sea the formation of the sub-surface Arctic Water Mass has been explained (Chapter 7) as the result of circulation and mixing processes similar to those described above for a coastal estuary.

# CHAPTER NINE

# Future Work

In this book, an endeavour has been made to describe the kind of physical information available about the oceans at the present time. It has been illustrated with descriptions of some of the features of the ocean waters and of their circulation, but the reader will realize that these are only samples. For more complete information it would be necessary to consult more extensive texts, such as those listed in the bibliography, or the original literature. In concluding this presentation it will be pertinent to assess the state of our present knowledge and to indicate some of the information which we still need.

For the upper layer of the ocean, it is safe to say that we are acquainted with the main features of the circulation and of the distribution of water properties, but there are few oceanographers who are satisfied with the extent of their knowledge of even limited areas.

One of the first features of the upper-water structure described in this book was the thermocline. This occurs over most of the ocean but the reason for its continued existence is by no means clear. In low latitudes there is a net annual input of heat through the surface, and together with the mixing due to the wind this might be expected to produce a steady deepening of the thermocline. The evidence available over the past 100 years is that this is not occurring. As an explanation of this Stommel has suggested that the downward mixing of heat must be balanced by a net upward flow of cool deep water displaced by winter cooled water sinking off Greenland and in the Weddell Sea. This is a very reasonable suggestion for the basic mechanism but it still leaves to be explained the differences in depth and in temperature gradient in the thermo-cline zone between different regions. Unfortunately the rate of upward flow is estimated to be so small as to be unmeasurable with present methods (of the order of 100 m/year) and therefore we can only infer it from heat budget calculations. These are only very approximate, since our techniques for measuring the component terms of the heat budget leave much to be desired in fundamental soundness, accuracy and convenience for use.

Many of the problems of the upper layers are closely connected with the atmosphere; these are mainly problems in dynamic oceanography which will not be discussed here explicitly. To solve these problems requires quantitative observation of the behaviour of the surface currents. For example, the main character of the equatorial circulation is well established but we have very few measurements of the volume transports of the currents and fewer of their variation of speed or position with time, or their rate of response to changes in winds. It is not out of the question that other currents remain to be discovered. For instance, the Cromwell Current which lies only 50 m below the surface and has at least half the transport of the Gulf Stream was not discovered until 1952, and we do not yet know what happens to this major current at its eastern end near the Galapagos Islands. The Pacific South Equatorial Counter Current was only recognized in 1959, and is still not well documented. In the North Pacific it is still not clear whether there are two sub-gyres inside the main gyre as Sverdrup believed, or only the single main gyre as has been suggested recently.

Upwelling of subsurface water is important as it often brings to the surface the nutrients which promote the growth of plankton and hence of fish. Many of the regions of upwelling are known, but there may be others which are as yet unrecognized. In the exchange of water within the upper layer, downwelling in regions of convergence is also important. Such regions are less easy to locate than upwelling regions but are still important in the circulation of the upper layer. Our great lack of information here is of the rate of vertical flow in both processes, and there does not seem to be in view at present any practical direct method to measure it.

For the deep water we are even more poorly informed than for the upper water. For the Atlantic Ocean we do have a good idea of the general direction of movement of the main water masses, but have a much poorer knowledge of even the direction of flow of the deep waters of the Pacific and Indian Oceans. Stommel has put forward a hypothesis that in the deep water there is a strong flow along the west sides of the oceans, with branches eastward and poleward to supply the upward flow needed to maintain the thermocline. This west side flow is mainly southward from the Labrador Sea in the Atlantic and northward from the Southern Ocean in the Pacific and Indian Oceans. With regard to the speed of motion of the deep water we have little information for any ocean. Estimates of the age of the Atlantic subsurface water masses vary from 100 to 1000 years; this variation in itself is evidence of the uncertainty of our knowledge. Even the age gives an indication only of the average speed. The measurements with Swallow floats, limited as they are, demonstrate that the instantaneous speed is very variable. As stated before, the classical concept of a sluggish flow of deep water is certainly unrealistic and it is more likely that jets or filaments of fast moving water are a basic feature of the deep circulation.

Another way of saying that we do not know much of even the mean speed of the deep water is to say that we have little idea of the rate of formation of the water masses. For instance, is the North Atlantic Deep Water produced each year in small quantities, or is it formed cataclysmically at irregular intervals as Worthington has suggested? Or do both processes play their part?

The [TS] diagram has been described with its use for identifying subsurface water masses. These are believed to be formed at the surface, often in winter, as a result of heat and water exchange with the atmosphere. Over the period of 100 years for which oceanographic data suitable for comparison are available there have been marked variations in climatic conditions. It is remarkable that despite this the various water masses in the ocean have retained their oceanographic characteristics virtually unchanged. The "18°" water in the Atlantic is an example of what is almost a water type which has maintained its characteristics since the time of the *Challenger* expedition in 1873.

The physical properties of sea-ice and the reasons for its distribution are neither fully described nor understood. To nations in the higher northern latitudes, Canada, Scandinavia and Russia, the ability to move shipping in the North Atlantic, Arctic and adjacent waters is very important. Although significant advances have been made in forecasting ice conditions, this still cannot be done with certainty or very far ahead. One of the interesting techniques used for the first time in 1961 for surveying ice distributions was photography from a Tiros satellite. Although there are difficult problems still to be solved, such as those posed by cloud cover, this may well prove to be the most efficient and economical method for determining ice coverage, almost from hour to hour.

In connection with the propagation of sound in the ocean, both for military purposes and for fish detection, there are still a vast number of data required on temperature distribution both on the macroscopic scale and also on the smaller scales associated with turbulence.

To advance his knowledge of the oceans the physical oceanographer needs more data in two forms—simultaneous coverage over large areas (together with meteorological data), and time-series observations over periods of the order of a year at least in selected localities. It is quite clear that there are never going to be enough oceanographers and ships to satisfy the requirements and the only possible way in which these extra data are going to be obtained is by using unmanned oceanographic observing buoys in large numbers. Work has started seriously on the problems of design and manufacture of such buoys in the last few years, but it will be some time before the flow of data from them becomes significant.

For such buoys, the designer faces a number of difficulties.

He is required to make an automatic device to measure temperature and salinity, etc., at a time when manually operated instruments for use from ships are still in their infancy. Buoys have to store large quantities of information, or preferably telemeter it to a base station frequently so that if a buoy is lost its store of information is not lost with it. There are also obvious problems in mooring such buoys so that they will withstand any weather. A more serious problem is to obtain sufficient channels in the radio frequency spectrum for telemetry.

For shipboard use there are many requirements for instruments. Continuous measurement of temperatures as a function of depth to 1500 m, through the main thermocline, would be desirable. This should preferably be to the precision to be expected of electrical thermometers but even a deep bathythermograph would be helpful despite its lower precision. *In situ* measurement of salinity to an accuracy of $\pm 0 \cdot 05\%_0$ or better in the upper 200 m, and to $\pm 0 \cdot 02\%_0$ to 1000 m or more would assist oceanographers in the study of the water structure. The present method of sampling now and measuring salinity later is slow and crude; immediate indication and recording as a function of depth would permit the oceanographer to see what he was getting on the spot, and to adjust his survey as necessary to make the best use of his ship time, and perhaps to follow particular features in space and time. The successful development of such instruments requires the combination of an assessment of the kind and accuracy of data required, the services of skilled instrument designers, and an appreciation of the conditions under which the instruments have to be used at sea.

It is clear that there are many intriguing problems yet to be solved in physical oceanography. There are extensive programmes of observation to be planned and instruments to be developed so that they may be carried out. The study and interpretation of the data and the comparison with theoretical studies will yield a fuller understanding of the ocean circulations and, we can be sure, will reveal further problems to be investigated. Much of the research will be carried out by oceanographers who have no other motive than to improve their understanding of the behaviour of the oceans. The individual who likes to see some practical application for the new knowledge can be assured that it will at once be seized upon by those concerned with urgent practical questions in the development of fisheries, the solution of waste disposal problems and in coastal engineering.

# Suggestions for Further Reading

The following texts may be consulted for more detailed information on some of the topics discussed in the present book and related subjects:

VON ARX, W. S.; *An Introduction to Physical Oceanography*, Addison Wesley, 1962, p. 422. A stimulating introduction to many aspects of physical oceanography, with special emphasis on current measurement and the use of scale models. Also includes study questions and an historical list of significant events in the marine sciences.

BURLING, R. W.; *Dynamical Oceanography*, Pergamon Press, 1966. The companion volume to the present one, describing the dynamical approach through the laws of physics.

DEFANT, A.; *Physical Oceanography*, Pergamon Press, 1960, p. 1319. An advanced level text. Volume I, Pt. 1 is descriptive while Pt. 2 and all of Vol. II are dynamical.

DIETRICH, G. and KALLE, K.; *Allgemeine Meereskunde*, Gebrüder Borntraeger, Berlin, 1957, p. 492. An account of physical and chemical oceanography.

HACHEY, H. B.; *Oceanography and Canadian Atlantic Waters*, Fisheries Research Board of Canada Bulletin No. 134, Ottawa, 1961, p. 120. A summary of developments in physical oceanography in Canadian Atlantic waters.

HILL, M. N. (Ed.); *The Sea: Ideas and Observations*, Interscience, Vol. I, 1962, p. 864. Physical oceanography. A collection of advanced papers on dynamical oceanography and energy transmission.
Vol. II, 1963, p. 554. Composition of sea-water. Comparative and descriptive oceanography. Further advanced papers on chemical, synoptic and biological oceanography.

KEEN, M. J.; *Submarine Geology*, Pergamon Press, 1966, Primarily concerned with the shape, structure, and sediments of the ocean basins.

ROUCH, J.; *Traité d'Océanographie Physique*, Payot, Paris, Vol. II, 1946, p. 349. L'eau de mer. The properties of sea-water and their distributions in the oceans.
Vol. III, 1948, p. 413. Les mouvements de la mer. Waves, tides and currents.

Rouch, J.; *Les Découvertes Océanographiques Modernes*, Payot, Paris, 1959, p. 251. A summary of more recent work in various aspects of physical and geological oceanography.

Stommel, H.; *The Gulf Stream*, University of California Press, 2nd Edn. 1964, p. 248. Both a description of this ocean feature and an excellent introduction to physical oceanography for upper year undergraduates and graduate students in physics.

Sverdrup, H. U., Johnson, M. W. and Fleming, R. H.; *The Oceans, their Physics, Chemistry and General Biology*, Prentice-Hall, New York, 1946, p. 1087. A comprehensive reference book on all aspects of oceanography. The most used text in the field at present.

*Instruction Manual for Oceanographic Observations*; U.S. Navy Hydrographic Office, Publ. No. 607, Washington, D.C., 1955, p. 210. A description of routine oceanographic procedures at sea and of standard instruments.

The classical papers in oceanography are scattered through many scientific journals and reports of expeditions. Many of the recent papers may be found in:

*Deep Sea Research*, Pergamon Press, Oxford (since 1953).

*Journal du Conseil* (from 1926) and *Annales Biologiques* (from 1939), Cons. Perm. Inter. pour l'Explor. de la Mer, Copenhagen.

*Journal of the Fisheries Research Board of Canada*. Ottawa (since 1934).

*Journal of Geophysical Research*. Amer. Geophys. Union, Richmond, Virginia (since 1959).

*Journal of Marine Research*. Sears Foundation for Marine Research, New Haven, Connecticut (since 1939).

*Limnology and Oceanography*. Amer. Soc. of Limnology and Oceanography, Lawrence, Kansas (since 1956).

*Transactions*, Amer. Geophys. Union, Washington, D.C. (1920 to 1958).

Two annual reviews of aspects of oceanography are:

Barnes, Harold (Ed.); *Oceanography and Marine Biology. An Annual Review*, George Allen and Unwin, London. (from Volume I, 1963.)

Sears, Mary (Ed.); *Progress in Oceanography*, Pergamon Press, Oxford. (from Volume I, 1964.)

# Index

196